THE BOY WHO LOVED APPLES

Amanda Webster grew up in Kalgoorlie, Western Australia. She graduated from the University of Western Australia as a doctor, but left medicine to raise a family with her husband. Amanda turned to writing after her son's illness; subsequently her work has appeared in several US literary journals. Amanda lives in Sydney with her husband and two of her three children.

The Boy Who Loved Apples

a mother's battle
with her son's anorexia

AMANDA WEBSTER

TEXT PUBLISHING MELBOURNE AUSTRALIA

textpublishing.com.au

The Text Publishing Company
Swann House
22 William Street
Melbourne Victoria 3000
Australia

First published in Australia by The Text Publishing Company, 2012

Cover by WH Chong
Page design by Imogen Stubbs
Typeset by J&M Typesetting
Printed and bound in Australia by Griffin Press, an Accredited ISO AS/NZS 14001:2004 Environmental Management System printer

National Library of Australia Cataloguing-in-Publication entry:
Author: Webster, Amanda
Title: The boy who loved apples : a mother's battle with her son's anorexia.
ISBN: 9781921922695 (pbk.)
ISBN: 9781921961113 (ebook)
Subjects: Webster, Amanda.
Anorexia nervosa—Patients—Australia—Biography.
Anorexia nervosa—Patients—Australia—Family relationships.
Anorexia in adolescence—Patients—Biography.
Anorexia in children—Patients—Biography.
Anorexia nervosa—Patients—Rehabilitation.
Eating disorders in adolescence.
Eating disorders in men.
Dewey Number: 616.85262092

This book is printed on paper certified against the Forest Steward-ship Council® Standards. Griffin Press holds FSC chain of custody certification SGS-COC-005088. FSC promotes environmentally responsible, socially beneficial and economically viable management of the world's forests

For Kevin, Riche, Andy and Louise
And in memory of Ava Margaret Webster

Author's note
Some identifying details have been changed
to protect the privacy of individuals.

Prologue

I magine for a moment that you are an Australian woman who has just given birth in the New York Hospital maternity ward. It is the spring of 1991. Your husband, also an Australian, helps you into a wheelchair. He balances an overnight bag on your lap. Then he scoops your newborn son—your *American* son—from the crib and hands him to you.

Tense the muscles in your arms and gather your son to your chest, amazed once more at the delicate weight of him. Shift your hand beneath his head and wonder: are you old enough at thirty-one to care for a child?

Before you leave, you cast your eyes over the wilting bouquet of flowers on the locker next to your bed and take one last look out the window of room 635 at the 59th Street Bridge. *Your city*, you whisper to your child. Such a tiny baby, such a massive city. Your husband wheels the two of you into the elevator, down to the entrance foyer, past the armed security guard and out to the street, where he hails a yellow taxicab to take you back to the Upper West Side. Back to your new life as a parent.

In your apartment high above Broadway, you record your baby's birth weight (7 lb 12 oz) and length (21 inches) in a baby book with a glossy black cover. You write your obstetrician's name—Dr Gubernik—in careful black print, and those of the two midwives—Pamela and Roseanne—who sponged your forehead with cool water and encouraged you to push. You paste in the newborn identification sheet—your right index fingerprint is just a smudge between the perfect impressions of your son's feet.

On his second night home, your son sleeps between you: your husband records this in scrawly blue handwriting on the 'Sleeping pattern' page. All three of you enjoy a charmed sleep. Your husband plays Carly Simon, Enya or Dire Straits each evening, because this is the music you listened to during your pregnancy. He thinks it will be familiar and soothing to his son and you love him for this. He doesn't know you played the music to soothe yourself as much as your unborn son, convinced you would somehow hurt him. Fretting because you failed to eat all the fruit and vegetable portions recommended in *What to Expect When You're Expecting* and didn't exercise as much as you could have; dwelling on the glass or two of wine you drank before you knew you were pregnant. Sometimes not even Carly Simon could slow the fearful beating of your heart.

This is your first child and you want to do everything by the book, so you paste a news clipping onto the blank page titled World Events—an article from your husband's *Wall Street Journal*. In years to come it will remind you, should you wish to know, that soon after your son's birth the Dow Jones Index rose by 17.58 points to close for the first time above 3000. Whatever that means. Of more interest is the report of US troops in northern Iraq and UN officials in search of Baghdad's nuclear and chemical arsenal. You wipe newsprint from your fingers, smell glue, unaware of the way the story of this year will echo in your son's life so many years into the future.

What you do know is this: you will do everything in your power to keep your child from harm. You will lock doors and windows. Fasten the seatbelt in his pram, always. Take him to the paediatrician for checkups. On your return to Australia, you will teach him to look to the right, look to the left, and look to the right again before he crosses the road to the private boys' school where you think he will be happy.

Where, at first, he is. Aged eight, he wins an academic scholarship. You smile and hug him and hope he doesn't detect your concern. Is this achievement too great a burden for such young shoulders? There's nothing you can do about this, so you concentrate your efforts where you can make a difference. Wholesome TV shows only, apart from a small lapse when Pokémon and Digimon somehow get their animated feet in the door. Nutritious meals—Weetbix for breakfast, Vegemite and cheese sandwiches for lunch, sausage and three veg for dinner, and fruit, always fruit, for snacks. When your son complains of an episode of bullying, you apply your lipstick—an indignant red—and march to the headmaster's office. You teach your son about stranger danger.

And you will learn that no matter how hard you try to protect your child you can never do enough. Your son will develop anorexia before he turns twelve and for months, years even, you will believe it is not nameless strangers who have proved to be the danger, but you and your husband.

Well-meaning acquaintances and friends alike will ask, 'Do boys get anorexia?' You will say, 'Yes.' (*Obviously.*) And then they will ask, 'How did he get it?' They will ask this because most, secretly, will consider you somehow at fault.

You will agree. You will compile a list of every mistake that you and your husband have ever made, believing that somewhere in that list you will find the answer to the question.

At least, this is how it was for me for a very long time.

Riche looked at the high brushwood fence as if it enclosed a gulag. 'I'm not going in there,'—the lines on his face a roadmap of fear—'you can't make me.'

I hesitated. I felt like I was having one of those weird dreams where you suddenly find yourself naked in the street or peeing in public. In fact I was standing with my eleven-year-old son outside a Brisbane eating disorder clinic called Footprints of Angels. It was January 2003 and my other children, nine-year-old Andy and six-year-old Louise, were at home in Mullumbimby, 150 kilometres to the south. I'd left them with their father—my husband—with whom I was not well pleased.

The place didn't look like a clinic. The fence, the unmarked letter-box and the discreet side entrance gave it more the appearance of a suburban brothel, a place where people came and went unobserved, a place of secrets, a place with stigma attached. But this was no time for squeamishness. Riche had been dangerously thin for three months and was showing signs of cardiac compromise. His pulse rate had been dropping; he got dizzy when he stood. I knew from my medical training that he was at risk of sudden death from cardiac arrest. I opened the gate.

'In we go.' I tried to sound purposeful. I tried to act as if my skin, stretched thin and tight over my body, didn't feel like the only thing holding me together.

My son flicked ash blond hair off his cadaverous face and shook his head, his expression blank, unreachable: a will-o'-the-wisp. His blue Mambo T-shirt hung from coathanger shoulders, and the light grey trousers he'd favoured since he was eight revealed the abrupt angles of his hips and the bony knobs of his ankles. These were trusted clothes, one of his anorexia uniforms, clean and calorie-free. On his feet were brown leather sandals, easy to scuff on and off without undoing the buckles.

'It's either here or hospital.' I tried to make it sound like a reminder, but even I could hear the threat in my voice.

Riche let his hair fall forward to cover his face and shuffled through the gate. I followed him into a well-tended garden. The scent of jasmine and gardenias hung heavy over a patch of neatly mown grass. On the far side, an old jacaranda tree shaded a picnic table. To our right stood the house, a classic Queenslander, built high off the ground on stilts. The open area underneath had been enclosed to make a room. Through the window I saw some comfortable-looking chairs and a large worktable. We made our way down a red brick pathway to a staircase tacked on sideways along the front of the house. The creak of the steps under my feet as we made our way up to the reception could have been the sound of my fear.

If the building looked like a bordello from the outside, the interior was straight out of a suburban beauty salon. Calming shades of pink, powder blue and pale lemon covered the walls. The sofas were awash with chintzy cushions. Angel figurines reclined on the desk, perched on the bookshelf, swung from the doorknobs and eyed me insouciantly from the coffee table. A host of angels, all female. Not an archangel in sight.

Riche scowled as he took in the oestrogen-charged decor. A receptionist confirmed our details and asked us to wait. I took a seat at the end of a sofa under the serene gaze of a celestial being; Riche shuddered and remained standing. I knew by now that nothing I could say would shake his belief that previous visitors—meat eaters, perhaps—had carelessly littered the sofa with stray calories. Riche believed that if he sat down these microscopic cluster bombs of energy would penetrate his skin and colonise his cells, and he would swell up like a fly-blown carcass. Rather than risk this, he paced back and forth, burning calories. A victory march for the illness that was sucking the life from him.

Wraithlike girls with perilous clavicles drifted through the room, their footsteps mere whispers against the dark wooden boards. They were all teenagers, older than Riche; there were no boys at all. Horrified, I stared at their skinny bodies, their tight, pinched expressions. *Controlling, manipulative.* I had discarded most of my eighties medical-school stereotypes after observing my son's decline; now they reared their ugly and misleading heads again. I almost started up out of the chair: Riche didn't belong here.

But as he circled the room, stopping only to allow one of the girls to pass, his body told another story. He looked as frail as any of them, as if the lightest of touches could fell him. He was one of them. He did not fit the stereotype because the stereotypes were wrong. I settled back onto the sofa and concentrated on the steady in and out of my breath.

The click of heels sounded in the hallway, and a woman appeared. She looked mid to late forties, about my age, but belonged to a glossier version of womanhood. She had the self-assured air I associated with women whose physical attributes—blonde hair, generous breasts— attract attention. Another mother, I thought, but anyone could see from her bright cotton print dress and her silken sheaf of hair that her daughter wasn't as sick as Riche. Caring for him left me with neither time nor energy for mascara and nail polish. My crumpled shirt, faded jeans and dark roots spoke of self-neglect. The woman looked at me and proffered a lipsticked smile.

'I'm Jan,' she held out her hand, 'the director.'

I felt a tremor as the fragile scaffolding of my hope collapsed inside me. Jan wasn't the suit-attired professional I had expected. She looked more like someone I would go to lunch with. How could she help my son? But somebody had to. I scrambled to my feet and shook hands.

Jan took us to the green room, where a green fabric angel, too flimsy to work miracles of any kind, hung from the green door. This place was big on colour coordination. Inside, the dim lighting and the frenetic floral of the verdant upholstery gave the room a vaguely threatening feel. Riche loitered near the door. His enormous dulled eyes took in the room.

'It's safe to sit down, Riche,' Jan said. 'The chair won't hurt you.'

Jan's understanding of Riche's unvoiced fears instilled a measure of comfort in me. Riche glared at her but consented to perch next to me on the sofa, well away from the cushions. Who knew how many calories lurked among all those ruffles? Living with an anorexic, I had found, was like living in France: a few months of immersion and you became fluent in the language.

A young woman sat in an armchair in the corner of the room. Her face had a fresh, scrubbed look and her hair, almost as blonde as Jan's, was tied in a high ponytail. Sonia, Jan said; one of the therapists.

Jan turned to Riche. 'So why did Mum bring you to see me?'

Riche shrugged and looked at his feet. I shifted in my seat, desperate to find the angle from which Riche's silence did not look like denial. When I had made the appointment the receptionist told me the clinic only took patients who accepted that they were sick. This didn't make sense to me—wasn't denial a characteristic of the illness? I suppressed the thought in much the same way as a child squashes Jack, his kinetic energy coiled, back in the box only to pop up later. I didn't get to make the clinic's rules. And now it looked like the game was up.

Riche's silence continued. I kept quiet, not wanting to be one of those parents who speaks for their children, for a good three seconds. Then: 'He's lost weight. He won't eat.'

Jan nodded and leaned forward. 'You're emaciated, Riche.' She spoke in a no-nonsense voice, almost cheerfully. Might as well lay the facts on the green (*yes!*) table. 'Perhaps Mum can tell me what's been happening.'

I took a breath and cleared my throat. 'It's complicated,' I said. 'We've made many mistakes.'

I'd easily rejected the notion that Riche's illness was caused by a controlling, manipulative temperament because he had never been that kind of child—quite the opposite. But another medical-school maxim, that dysfunctional parents cause anorexia, was less easily rejected. It is a common belief that a child's behaviour reflects parenting skills—any mother with a screaming two-year-old in a supermarket knows how that one goes. And like any mother I naturally concluded that my husband and I had messed up. So I confessed to Jan. Every disagreement, death, dietary quirk and relocation I could recall came tripping out.

As diagnostic tools, a medical school professor once told us, stethoscopes, microscopes, laparoscopes and colonoscopes are all well and good, but nothing compares with the retrospectoscope. Hindsight is always 20/20. Now, through the retrospectoscope, the details of my confession look highly circumstantial. They are the small slip-ups many parents without a sick child would admit to, and at the very most they are only part of the story. But back then, I found my culpability both obvious and overwhelming.

When I'd finished I said, 'Does he really have anorexia?' Still, with the gaunt evidence sitting right there beside me, the unreliable emotion of hope bloomed.

'Classic case,' Jan said without a second's hesitation. 'But you and Kevin aren't to blame. Having an anorexic child doesn't make you a bad parent.'

Not my fault? Not Kevin's? I wanted to believe her but Riche hadn't been raised in a vacuum. Surely there needed to be some reckoning of his childhood. Furthermore, if we hadn't caused

Riche's anorexia, who or what had? This question would continue to haunt me. For years the feeling of blame—directed at myself and at Kevin—dragged me down like shackles.

For now I said nothing.

Jan turned to Riche. 'I know you have a voice in your head that says you're fat, but it's lying. We call that voice the negative mind. Can you hear it?'

Riche shook his head, and I steeled myself for Jan's inevitable rejection.

She said, 'We can offer Riche a place in the program.'

'But you don't take people in denial.'

'Usually, no, but Riche is on the verge of acceptance and frankly, we need to act. It's a race against the clock.'

With a rush of gratitude I realised I had found a place where Riche would be treated—and treated compassionately—without being institutionalised. I knew from experience, however, what a mistake it could be to rely on someone else's supposed expertise. When it came to anorexia, there were too many unknowns, too few experts and too many unvalidated theories. I wouldn't just hand over responsibility for my child and hope it would turn out all right.

For now, however, Footprints was my best option. And so, while Riche sat silently beside me, the negotiation began.

Jan told me that Riche needed a weekly program of four counselling sessions with Sonia and one session with the dietician. I said we'd start with two counselling sessions and did he really need to see the dietician? Jan said yes. I said I couldn't see the point for an eleven-year-old boy: Riche didn't prepare the meals; I did. Besides, ignorance about calories and nutrition didn't seem to be the problem. Quite the reverse—he read energy charts and food labels like a professional. Jan said something along the lines of the dietician working to improve Riche's relationship to food. I thought *bullshit*. But I said yes, which goes to show either that I didn't understand the basic principles of consumerism, or that I was scared witless.

With no government funding, compassionate treatment came at a price. Each session would cost $110. The Day Program that Riche would be unable to attend because of his fear of footloose calories would have cost an additional $50 per day. Protein powder for supplementary shakes, if needed, cost $40 per week. Our private health fund would cover the dietician's appointment but not the counselling sessions.

The cost to attend full time amounted to $750 per week—this in a country with a free public healthcare system, albeit one with big black holes such as the lack, in 2003, of outpatient facilities to treat sufferers of anorexia and support their families. Not exactly a bargain, but we could afford it. I would have mortgaged my soul to get Riche back. The happy, healthy Riche.

Jan went on to tell me I would be excluded from Riche's sessions and would not be given any feedback. Again I failed to see the logic. If I wasn't to blame, why the need to exclude me? Especially when Riche would be in my care twenty-three hours a day. Asking him to eat a cheese and Vegemite sandwich was akin to asking my husband to eat steak seasoned with cyanide: I reckoned I might need some help too. Instead, it seemed, I would be left to steer in the dark, sidelined to the roles of cook, chauffeur and cheerleader.

No, I silently promised myself. Not if I could help it. At the very least I could educate myself. Borders and I were about to embark on a very close relationship.

We moved on to logistics. Would I move to Brisbane? No I wouldn't; I had two other children. Didn't I think the driving would tire Riche? And how would he control his negative mind without Sonia's daily coaching? I would see how we went. *If a twenty-something-year-old with a twelve-month counselling course can do this, why couldn't I, a doctor with six years' training, be taught?* is what I thought. *And who would help Riche on weekends?*

'What about school work?' I said.

'No school.' Jan shook her head. 'Riche needs all his energy to fight this illness.' It was the right advice but, I would discover, the wrong reason.

'How long is it going to take?'

'It could take five years, longer even.'

I closed my eyes and let myself sink into the blackness behind my lids. My body felt heavy and lumpish. Five years? Riche's illness would rob him of his childhood. He would never again 'watch with glittering eyes the whole world around' as Roald Dahl urges in *The Minpins*, an early gift from Riche's godmother. How would he discover the 'greatest secrets'? How would he find the magic?

I looked at Jan. 'Anorexia is going to change our lives, isn't it?'

'Forever.' Jan returned my gaze without smiling. 'This illness can break up marriages.'

When the front door of our Mullumbimby cottage opened and slammed shut seven months earlier, another door—the door to our old life—closed, unobserved. I noticed only the smell of burning wood from the neighbours' bonfire and the sound of Riche's signature entrance—two dull thuds as his discarded sandals hit the floor. He hurtled, all gangly arms and legs, past the diningroom table to draw up beside me at the stove.

'I'm going to catch the plague,' he said, wild eyed and panting. He ran a hand through his thick blond hair, leaving a charcoal smudge on his forehead. 'Next door's bonfire disturbed a nest of rats and Sally caught one.'

'Rats? That explains the barking.' I turned down the gas so the rice wouldn't boil over.

'You're missing the point—Sally dropped the rat at my feet and licked me.' Riche stepped closer to me. 'People die from the plague, you know.'

His urgency surprised me. I looked at my son. He was small for an eleven-and-a-half-year-old, lean and muscular, and he gave the impression of constant, restless motion, like a windmill buffeted by a gale. Despite the wintry chill he wore shorts that ended mid-thigh, exposing knobby knees, and one of the short-sleeved Mambo T-shirts that would soon become his uniform. Pneumonia seemed more likely than plague, although he didn't look cold. Red patches flared on his cheeks, and damp tendrils of hair clung to his forehead. After only three months of country life, he looked like he'd lived here forever. He would have been unable to resist the temptation to get close to the bonfire, prodding at it with sticks and enjoying the spectacle of the petrol-fuelled flames that shot from the paddock into the starry night.

'That dog's a menace to the wildlife,' I said. 'And what have you done with your brother and sister?'

'Andy said he'd bring Louise home.' Riche gave me an earnest look. 'Sally can't help chasing the wallabies Mum, it's her instinct. But what if I've caught the plague?'

That was my son: always ready to defend an animal, but quite prepared to abandon his younger siblings. 'What plague? You've lost me.'

'It looked like a Norwegian rat. *Rattus norvegicus*, they carry the bacteria that causes the plague.'

The rice was cooked and ready to drain. I switched off the gas and lifted the saucepan.

'You're not listening.'

'Sorry.' I emptied the saucepan into a strainer. 'I don't follow you.'

'She licked me.' Riche spoke slowly and stressed each word. 'And she would have had the bacteria in her saliva from holding the rat.'

He stuck his right index finger in his mouth and made his cheek pop loudly. He repeated this several times. Cheek popping was a new and only slightly less annoying habit than its predecessor, tennis ball bouncing. For weeks our hundred-year-old wooden cottage had shuddered with each bounce for up to an hour at a time, several times a day.

'You'll be fine,' I said. 'But I won't be if you keep doing that.'

Riche started pacing restlessly while he clenched and unclenched his fists. I balanced the rice strainer on the rim of the saucepan and looked at my son. He stared back at me, his eyes unblinking, the pupils dilated black pools of fear.

'Riche, it's 2002, not 1602. And it happened in Europe. Nobody's ever died of the plague in Australia.' I tried to sound authoritative; as a doctor I should know these things. But after twelve years of fulltime motherhood, I was rusty on data such as the demographics of the plague.

Riche, on the other hand, seemed to be an expert. 'Not true.' He switched to a matter-of-fact tone. 'A number of deaths were recorded in Australia in the early 1900s.'

His expertise was hardly surprising. At five years of age, asked to name his favourite animals, he had listed single-celled organisms alongside the dinosaurs and sharks.

There was a familiar scrape and shuffle as my mother appeared in the doorway with her walking frame. My father moved forward, took her frame, and guided her to the heavy wooden chair we'd chosen for its stability. My mother lurched the final step or two and grasped the broad flat arms, then lowered her treacherous body onto the cushions. I took plates from the cupboard and a handful of cutlery from the drawer by the sink. When I looked back at Riche, he was watching my mother with narrowed eyes. His expression was fearful. Or disgusted; I couldn't quite tell.

'You're going to be fine,' I said, 'we'll talk later. Your dad'll be home any minute.'

'Great.' Anger tightened his features. 'Another weekend of hassling.' He turned and went into the bathroom.

Great, I echoed. I was not looking forward to the resumption of Kevin's argument with his smarter and infinitely more sensitive son.

My mother looked around as if seeing the room for the first time. The previous year a sudden, severe headache and vomiting had sent her to hospital. Doctors diagnosed a bleed from an aneurysm and gave her a fifty-fifty chance of a catastrophic re-bleed. I left the children with Kevin and flew to Perth, where my parents lived. The doctors wanted to insert a coil into the leaky vein and sought permission from my father, a doctor, rather than my still-conscious and coherent mother. A gesture of respect, I suppose. My father asked my opinion and I agreed and went to see my mother.

She was lying on a trolley, dressed in a theatre gown, her hair caught up in a paper cap. She smiled when she saw me and asked if I would mind applying her depilatory cream to her upper lip after the procedure. Hormone therapy, she said, was causing hair growth. It was the last completely intelligent thing she ever said to me.

It's a truism in medical circles that treatment often goes wrong in the case of doctors' families and it was certainly true with my mother. Afterwards the doctor told us that the procedure had been difficult. Over a period of seven hours he'd attempted many times to insert the coil and in the end resorted to blocking the offending blood vessel with a glue-like substance. At one point, my mother had suffered an episode of severe bradycardia, a dramatic slowing of the heart, that deprived her brain of oxygen.

She lay in a coma for several weeks and woke mildly brain-damaged. I was furious with the doctor, who I thought had persisted with the procedure for longer than advisable in a woman with Mum's circulatory issues and history of high blood pressure.

The next procedure was neurosurgery, to relieve increased pressure in her skull. That was complicated by post-operative meningitis. The nursing staff told me her temperature had shot up to 43 degrees Celsius, the highest temperature the thermometer could measure. She remained unconscious and I suspected there would be further brain damage from the infection and the fever.

At this point I thought hard about how to proceed. I thought about Mum's age and her drastically compromised quality of life. She'd been an active woman, always involved in some church function or other, and those days were clearly over. I wanted supportive treatment only. Fluids and painkillers, intravenous antibiotics at the absolute outside.

I wanted the doctors to give her a chance to fight; I didn't want them venturing into medical heroics.

Instead the doctor ordered aggressive treatment—injection of antibiotics directly into the cerebrospinal fluid. She suffered another extended period of unconsciousness, followed by lengthy rehabilitation.

My mother came home in nappies, unstable on her feet, with a memory as reliable as candles in a snowstorm. The sliver of hope the neurosurgeon offered was that she should eventually be able to get around the house with the aid of a walking frame.

He wouldn't be finding any Christmas cards from me in his letterbox.

And he wouldn't be there to help my father care for my mother in their suburban Perth home. A nursing home wasn't an option—my mother thought these were the devil's own designs—and I lived on the other side of the continent nearly four thousand kilometres away. The only solution I could see was for my parents to leave Perth and come to live with me. I wanted to look after them, partly to make up for a petulant adolescence that came late, in my twenties, and stretched through my thirties.

But our self-important split-level Sydney home was hopeless for someone with a walking frame. And so, since an excess of any emotion—joy, anger, pride, grief: take your pick—can distort your vision and lead you to make extraordinary decisions, I decided to up sticks completely. Years later my daughter told me I said, 'Pack your bags and get in the car.' And I guess that's how it seemed. Swamped by emotions I barely understood, I fled my former life, a life of corporate dinners and swanky parties that no longer seemed relevant, and moved with the children to our holiday home in the bush near Mullumbimby in the Byron Shire.

Byron is alternative territory: a sixties freeze-frame where the citizens do downward dogs on the beach at dawn and have tantric sex in the twilight to the beat of a bongo drum. A place where vegan hippies can tell you the closing price of technology stock and a boy with Down Syndrome packs groceries at the checkout of the local supermarket. This was a place with room for everyone, including an old woman who walked with a frame and had slid a few notches down the IQ pole. Here my mother would sail into the irrepressibly golden sunset of her life surrounded by the five of us (six on weekends) in the patchouli-scented environment of a three-bedroom cottage.

Kevin was to commute weekly from his office in Sydney, flying the 780 kilometres to the holiday house each weekend and returning to work on Monday.

That's not so much to ask, is it?

○

My commuter husband arrived home in his double-breasted suit and starched shirt while I was serving the chicken tagine. He looked like he'd stepped out of a Hugo Boss billboard. He left his briefcase by the door and came into the room. Minnie, our cocker spaniel, flew into a frenzy of yelping and leaping.

'Can you call your dog?' Kevin said to me. 'I don't want my suit wrecked.' He hoisted Louise onto his hip with one arm and held Andy close with the other, and the three of them swapped news.

I subdued Minnie and returned to the casserole. Riche avoided looking at Kevin and shunted a piece of chicken around his plate. I wanted to shake some sense into Kevin's good-looking head. Why did intermittent fathering encourage him to serialise his disagreement with his son? He hadn't witnessed the argument between his mother and Riche. What made him so sure Riche should apologise?

Andy grinned at his dad. The physical resemblance between father and son struck me as it always did: small dark eyes, a thick lower lip and strong bone structure, but Andy's skin was olive, like my mother's. Riche, on the other hand looked like me; Louise was a hybrid. Genetics: you get what you're given.

Kevin looked over at Riche and said, voice loud so that Riche would know he was being spoken to, 'How's your week, mate?'

Riche didn't look up. 'Fine.'

Kevin's face took on a determined set and I flashed my husband a warning look. He shrugged, leaned forward, gave me a kiss which I returned with a half-hearted peck on the cheek. 'You hungry?'

'Famished.' He sniffed the spicy steam that rose in lazy spirals from the casserole. 'But don't give me any rice. My surfboard sinks when I sit on it.'

I snorted. Kevin's recent preoccupation with the low-carbohydrate Atkins Diet annoyed me. Why abandon a whole food group when all he need do was give up snacks and second helpings?

I spooned a modest serving of the casserole and rice onto a plate for my father. 'Here's dinner.' I waited for him to put his crossword puzzle away before I set the plate down in front of him.

'Is this for me?' my father said. 'It looks great, whatever it is. But it needs sweet chili sauce.'

My father thought everything needed sweet chili sauce. He shook thick orange globs of it over the chicken. I noted his trim figure with satisfaction. He had ballooned in the eight months he had cared for my sick mother in their Perth home and I was horrified: I saw it as a sign of self-neglect, a health issue, so I had assumed the role of dietary police since his arrival in Byron. At my insistence, he substituted artificial sweetener for the three teaspoons of sugar in his tea, spread his breakfast toast with Vegemite—lots of low-calorie B vitamins— but no butter (*you're not meant to spread butter like it's cheese, Dad*), and ate light everything instead of full-cream. In three months I had whittled my father down to a size he hadn't been since his thirties. I didn't stop to think about the message this conveyed to my children.

My mother sat at the end of the table. During my childhood she'd been a fiend for hygiene—wash your hands before dinner and put the dog outside—but now it was one bite for my mother and one for Minnie, who delicately took the chicken from the same fork.

Riche watched from across the table. My mother's illness bothered him more than Andy or Louise, perhaps because he was older. The demented chatter, the walking frame, the shit-filled adult nappies that clogged the bathroom bin: he took it all in. 'I don't ever want to go to hospital,' he'd say. 'Look what it did to Grandma.' He was right. My father and I were both doctors but my mother was no advertisement for our profession.

An hour passed before I could talk privately with Kevin. We were tidying up the kitchen.

'I'm worried about Riche,' I said.

'Can I use steel wool on this?' Kevin started scrubbing. 'What's up?'

'You know how he latches onto an idea and can't seem to drop it?'

Kevin made a mocking sound, a staccato 'p' released with a puff of air. 'He's stubborn—like his mother.'

'Be serious.' I flicked him with the tea towel. 'Tonight it was extreme, even for Riche.' I gave him the *Reader's Digest* version of the rat story.

'What are you going to do?'

'Don't know. But I think you should pull your head in.'

Kevin lifted his shoulders to his ears and dipped his chin. 'I'm pulling my head in,' he said, his expression like Minnie's when she wanted to play.

'Funny.' My not-amused look bounced off my husband's thick skin. 'Why should Riche have to apologise to your mother? She's the one who was out of line.'

'Remind me what she said.' Kevin pulled the plug and peeled off his rubber gloves.

'You know exactly what she said, and you know it's just the sort of thing your mother's likely to say. There's no reason to think Riche's lying. Anyway, Andy and Louise heard the whole thing and they say he's telling the truth.'

Kevin opened the kitchen door and went out to the side veranda.

I followed. We leaned against the railing and looked up at the stars. The smell of burning wood from the neighbours' bonfire was stronger here. Fruit bats flew overhead, eerily silent except for the beating of their wings. I could see into two of the bedrooms, spot-lit tableaux: my father helping my mother into bed, Andy and Louise playing with plastic dinosaurs on the floor of the bedroom they shared. Riche was nowhere in sight.

'Can't Riche apologise for the sake of peace?' Kevin said. 'None of you have spoken to my parents in months. It's ridiculous.'

'You're ridiculous. Get *her* to apologise, and please leave Riche alone.'

Kevin sucked in a deep breath and then let it out in a long, slow hissing sound, as if releasing a valve. 'Sure,' he said. 'I won't ask him again. I promise.'

The day after Riche's supposed contact with medieval bugs, I came home from a shopping trip to find him on the carport steps with Kevin. Riche was shouting and punching the air, his shoulders hunched. His father stood on the top step, hands on hips, feet apart, looking down at his son. I got out of the car. Kevin flashed me a smile that stopped short of his eyes.

'Want help with the shopping?' he said in a nothing's-up voice.

I gave him a questioning look, a marital telegram he either missed or ignored as he carried the shopping bags into the house.

Riche kicked the vacated top step. 'Dad asked me why I can't be big enough to apologise.' He looked up. 'Why can't he take my side for a change?'

So much for Kevin's promise. I felt like one of those council workers who appears with a truckload of sand to clean up someone else's oil spill. 'He is on your side, he just doesn't like confrontation. Especially with his mother.'

'It's not fair.' Riche reached for his bike and climbed on. 'I'm going for a ride.'

I stormed in to Kevin. 'Big enough to apologise?' I said. 'That's brilliant. Wait until I've gone before you have a go at him?'

'Stop shouting,' Kevin said, and smirked. It was an unconscious habit. As a child he was told repeatedly, *Wipe that smile off your face or I'll wipe it off for you.* 'Mind if I go surfing?'

Mind? Be my guest. Stay out all day. Which he pretty much did. For the rest of the weekend, we treated each other with careful distance. Riche rode his bike or kept to himself in his room.

Over the next few weeks, as far as I could tell, Riche and Kevin stopped fighting. I was too busy to give it much thought. My mother's golden sunset life seemed to involve excessive quantities of shit, the occasional vomit and a lot of time—an hour each morning to shower and dress her. Moreover, three small bedrooms between six people, seven on weekends, took togetherness to an extreme, even with Riche sleeping in the closet-sized study.

One day I was peeling carrots at the sink, dreaming another life for myself that involved nights at the Cipriani in Missoni gowns. I was pondering my dress choice when Riche's voice brought me back to the chipped wooden cupboards and greasy gas burners of my kitchen. He was seated at the diningroom table.

'I think I'm depressed.' Frowning, he pointed at the magazine open in front of him. 'It says depressed children overeat to make themselves feel better. Then they end up obese.'

'What makes you say that?' His comment confused me. I recalled feeling anxious and depressed for long periods at a similar age but Riche didn't seem depressed. His intensity over the rat had worried me a few weeks before, but that seemed to have faded. Maybe he didn't laugh so much these days, but he wasn't moping around the house. Far from it: he spent hours outside, walking or riding his bike, surely not the behaviour of someone with depression.

But now Riche's face was crumpling. 'I feel bad inside,' and he rubbed at the tears spilling from his eyes. 'I feel bad because of Dad. It's like I was sailing on the ocean with him, and he tipped me overboard and left me out there with no way of getting to the shore.'

I walked over and hugged him. 'He doesn't realise what he's doing,' I said. 'I'll talk to him again.'

I wondered if I should take Riche to the doctor for antidepressants—horrible thought—or jolly him along; hope this was just one of his phases. In addition to not appearing depressed, Riche had a privileged life and two devoted parents. Despite his current behaviour, Kevin had been besotted with Riche ever since that spring morning in the New York Hospital maternity wing. Every weekend during those early months, Kevin stole precious hours away from his work at Merrill Lynch to walk, with Riche cocooned against his chest in a blue and white spotted Snugli, through Central Park to the Metropolitan Museum. Since then, he had shunted Thomas the Tank Engine over endless configurations of wooden track and shored up countless sandcastles on Balmoral Beach near our Sydney house. Admittedly, Kevin now seemed determined to scuttle his relationship with Riche. But seriously, clinically depressed? My much-loved son? Not possible.

Riche wriggled out of my arms and stepped back. 'What if I get fat?'

'You've nothing to worry about,' I said. 'You eat healthy food, you exercise, and you have good genes.'

It's tempting to look back at that woman with her head full of dreams and her hands full of carrots and convict her of complete idiocy. But who knew boys could get anorexia? It wasn't mentioned during my medical training. The famous male sufferers, actor Dennis Quaid and singer Daniel Johns, were yet to speak publicly about the illness. And how could anyone know that such an article in my son's hands was a trigger for the anorexia pointed, even then, like a gun at his head?

Riche came to me a week or so later with a local newspaper ad: a Northern Rivers Wildlife Carers training day. 'It's at the Drill Hall,' he pointed out. 'Can we go?'

'Great idea.' I was pleased to see some of his old enthusiasm return.

I signed us up, and we spent several weekends in dusty country halls learning bird, wallaby, possum, snake and bat care. Within a few weeks, injured and abandoned butcher birds, currawongs and rainbow parrots started to arrive in a deluge of feathers and squawk-ing mouths, victims of domestic animals or collisions with cars or windows. Most died. Each death seemed to hurt Riche deeply.

One day Riche and I were driving from our property to nearby Mullumbimby, the self-proclaimed 'biggest little town in Australia'. Sugar cane shimmered into the distance and Mount Chincogan loomed ahead, a sharp peak imprinted on a benign sky. At the crest of the hill, we passed the body of a wallaby. Riche whimpered. From the corner of my eye I saw him flinch.

'The government should ban cars,' he said. 'We should travel by foot or by horse.'

I asked him whether that wasn't a little extreme.

'No,' he replied. 'People are speciesist.'

'What?'

'Like racist.' Riche hunkered down in his seat. 'Except it's an attitude of superiority to other species instead of other races.'

I wondered if I had a modern day St Francis on my hands, or if saintliness itself was a dressed-up version of obsessive behaviour. If so, it didn't immediately trouble me. Riche's current concerns would go the way of previous obsessions such as Thomas the Tank Engine and Pokémon, now forgotten at the bottom of the toy basket after a long and tyrannical reign over the loungeroom floor. What didn't occur to me was that Riche's heightened concern for animal welfare signalled a seismic shift in his thinking. It reflected changes in the chemistry of his brain that made familiar objects take on unfamiliar meaning.

When we got home, I put the steak we'd just bought on the bench while I cleaned the meat tray. The eleven-year-old ascetic at my elbow stepped back, his face grim. Long-limbed and lean, he was dressed as usual in shorts and a Mambo T-shirt. His close-cropped hair stood in blond spikes, a caricature of shock. I picked the steak up, leaving a puddle of blood on the bench. Riche moaned and looked away.

'That's disgusting,' he said. 'I'm becoming a vegetarian. Do you know how many cows Americans consume each day?'

I shook my head. He quoted a figure and cited a source, then quizzed me on the number of acres needed to farm cows. Again, bottom of the class; he quoted another figure. I repacked the meat tray and sponged the bench. I most likely paid excessive attention to these tasks. Undeterred by my lack of interest, Riche informed me that if those same acres yielded crops for human consumption, the problem of world starvation would be solved.

Years later, when I searched for facts to verify his statement, I found supporting data from David Pimentel, a professor of ecology and agriculture. Ruminants in the US do indeed chew their way (twice) through enough grain to feed nearly 800 million people. Riche was right.

At the time I thought, *I'm just feeding the family*, and told my son that meat contains valuable iron and protein. Dentally speaking, I went on, we evolved as omnivores. Unlike Riche, I couldn't cite my long-forgotten source, if it ever existed. Nonetheless, I presented this 'fact' with a flourish—my evolutionary trump card.

Riche's previous bout of vegetarianism, the year before, had lasted two weeks, so I wasn't worried. Nor was I worried when he took to studying my recipe books. On the contrary, I was impressed by his diligence and recorded this activity as part of his curriculum in personal health and development, a Board of Studies requirement for the home schooling program we'd started earlier that year. His fascination for the calorie charts in the back of the books seemed unusual for an eleven-year-old boy, but I put it down to his superior intelligence, his enquiring mind. As the list of prohibited foods grew longer, a small fear niggled like a toothache in the midst of the maternal pride—so young to be an anti-junk-food crusader and environmental warrior.

Still, was it really a problem? There were plenty of nutritious foods left. There was tofu, for example, rubbery blocks of it bathed in its whey-like fluid littering the fridge; cheddar cheese ('make sure it's the healthy low fat'); rice; bread; lentils that I simmered in a broth spiced with turmeric, ginger and cumin. And, of course, apples. Riche had loved apples since he was a toddler. Pink Ladies, Red Delicious, Lady Williams and, especially, Fujis: Riche loved them all. He ate them two or three at a time. No way was he going to go hungry while apples grew on trees.

Riche's preoccupation with human evil grew and spilled over into his schoolwork. When I bought plain Bonds T-shirts for the boys to decorate with environmental slogans as part of a science project, Andy produced a fairly standard 'Save the Trees' design. Riche painted a black skull above a white cross and wrote in black marker pen:

Rain falling on my head
Unfortunately it was acid rain
And now I'm dead.

Later, I would see it as a sign: one of the undeniable symptoms of Riche's depression. At the time I found myself seduced and impressed by his precocious sensitivity. Besides, he seemed to balance this negativity with an increasing enthusiasm for physical activity. He joined the Mullumbimby Little Athletics Club and the Universal Self Defence Academy. He already belonged to the Spaghetti Circus. At home, he practised juggling with oranges stolen from the fruit bowl, his dedication earning him a spot in the annual show.

'I'm in an acrobatics routine too,' he said. 'I'm part of a human pyramid. The guy I stand on says I'm nice and light.'

That night I lay in bed listening to the wind rattle the windows and thought about those words. Nice and light. Eleven-year-old boys shouldn't be thinking that 'light' weight was 'nice'. They shouldn't be giving weight any thought at all. As far as I knew, Riche's dietary intake was healthy, but was it enough to fuel all that exercise?

I considered talking to him; I decided against it. I didn't want to talk a problem into existence. Or was it that the problem didn't exist as long as it remained unnamed?

Three months after the plague-rat bonfire there was an interaction in the waiting room of the Mullumbimby Veterinary Clinic that wasn't as easy to dismiss. I had weighed the dogs in order to calculate the correct dosage of worm medication, and the children decided it would be a good idea to weigh each other.

Andy was first up. He hopped on the rubber platform and watched the digits flicker. 'Twenty-six kilograms.' He looked at his brother. 'Your turn.'

Riche stepped on. We all watched the scale; I was as eager as he was to know his weight. The numbers rose to twenty-six and kept climbing. Riche reared back.

'You're twenty-nine kilograms,' Andy said in a matter-of-fact voice. 'Three more than me.'

Riche silently stepped off the scales and turned away from his brother. He looked at me, his face pale and shocked. 'It's too much.'

A moment of sudden panic. 'You're supposed to weigh more,' I said. 'You're nineteen months older.'

Riche stared past me, eyes vacant. He let himself out of the waiting room and started pacing up and down the pathway. Louise gave me an uncertain look and then climbed on the scales.

For the first time I saw my son as an onlooker might: a thin boy, irrationally convinced he was too fat and trying with all his fast-diminishing might to become thinner. I knew there was a word for that. I even allowed myself to think it in connection with Riche.

It sounded paranoid. I didn't mention my suspicion to Kevin.

But from then on Riche's intention to lose weight was crystal clear. He exercised like one possessed. By day, he practised the long jump in the sandpit and cartwheeled on our front lawn. By night, he did push-ups in the hallway and sit-ups in front of the television. He didn't stop until he went to bed.

Food preparation became a nightmare: Riche wouldn't eat meat;

no one else would eat tofu or lentils. Louise would eat chicken but not red meat. My father didn't like meat on the bone or rice (too bland even with sweet chili sauce). And none of them was keen on vegetables. My mother was the only one who ate everything within reach. And of course there was Minnie, waiting patiently at her side for forkfuls of meat.

The upshot was that when Riche requested tofu four nights a week, I took the path of least resistance and cooked his meal separately. I didn't stop to consider that by buying into his increasingly rigid food choices I was aiding and abetting an illness that would place its embargo on one food after another: that would, eventually, starve him to death given half a chance. I marinated the tofu in soy sauce, brown sugar and ginger, coated it with sesame seeds and flour, pan fried it and served it with steamed rice and salad on the side.

Riche usually ate it all. Then one night he left three cubes on his plate. The same thing happened the next night and the night after, until I asked him what was wrong with the tofu.

'You're giving me more than usual.' He avoided eye contact and wouldn't be convinced by my assurances. I wished I could figure out what was wrong with him.

My medical knowledge should have helped with raising a young family, even though I hadn't practised as a doctor in years, but it didn't. I knew I overreacted sometimes: once, I tried to get local officials at St Kitts in the Caribbean to re-open the airport in the middle of the night to evacuate Andy, then eighteen months old, after the doctor made a diagnosis of middle ear infection without the aid of an auroscope. *With this fever, it must be meningitis.* (At other times I underreacted. Kevin said he needed to be near death to get attention.) So again I dismissed the thought of anorexia: more overreacting. We were not the dysfunctional family described in the medical textbooks. Besides, I thought, boys don't get anorexia.

But when Riche cut back on apple I began to worry. He had always liked me to prepare his beloved apples. I would peel them

29

with a paring knife, removing only the thinnest layer of skin, and cut them into eight precise wedges. After years of practice I peeled like a professional. Not so Kevin, who used a vegetable peeler to slice off huge chunks with the same vigour as he carved the waves with his surfboard. All muscle and movement, no finesse. Riche hated the waste. So something was wrong for him to leave three pieces of apple.

'They fell on the floor.' He stared at me with empty eyes that seemed to have become more prominent in a face drained of colour, despite the hours he spent outside. His delicious squirrel cheeks had disappeared, and his hair (which for reasons that were unclear to me he refused to have cut) hung dull and lifeless halfway down his gazelle-like neck. I knew from his loose clothing that he had lost weight although I wasn't sure how much. I had never been good at recording those statistics. The excuses varied each day—a dog licked the apple; a fly landed on it; it tasted bad.

Now, years later, I check the carbohydrate, fibre, and fat counter in the back of one of my cookbooks. Raw, peeled apple (100 grams) contains twelve grams of carbohydrate, one gram of fibre, zero grams of fat, and—the kicker—205 kilojoules or forty-nine calories, eleven calories already sacrificed with the peel. I do the maths: three pieces of apple contain roughly nineteen calories.

Anorexic mythology: nineteen calories will make you fat.

By then Riche spent five hours each day striding up and down the rainforest trail behind the cottage, rarely coming in for a drink, despite the mid-thirties temperatures of an early summer.

'Did you eat breakfast this morning?' I quizzed him after one such walk.

'Yeah. Before you got up. Two pieces of toast with Promite.'

I hadn't seen any dirty plates in the sink but I knew Riche to be a truthful kid; I saw no reason to doubt his word.

Next, he asked to eat meals separately from the rest of the family.

'I don't like eating near meat-eaters.'

'No. You're making us feel like lepers.'

Riche followed me round the house, arguing his case: meat looked disgusting, the smell put him off his food, Grandma's eating habits upset him—which was understandable since they upset me too. In the midst of all this, Andy and Louise came in, looking for food; my father wanted to know if it was time to bring my mother to the table, and the dogs were waiting to be fed. I gave in. If eating alone was what it took to get Riche to eat, then so be it. He could sit on the roof if necessary.

Again I played unwittingly into the hands of the illness that had taken up residence in Riche's head. In letting him eat alone I gave it free rein to torture him while he ate, to convince him to hide or dispose of his food. And, of course, Riche didn't really eat alone. He ate with a hungry dog by his side.

○

One October morning I set Riche and Andy some schoolwork and then bundled Louise, Barbie schoolbag in hand, into the car. A feisty six-year-old needed the company of people who shared her passion for pink. She chatted while I drove past the sugarcane fields into Mullumbimby, and then out to the Shearwater Steiner School set against the backdrop of the Nightcap Ranges. Usually I loved the drive. But today, when I looked at the cane stalks, I thought about a recent lecture from Riche on the evils of sugarcane: it destroyed native habitats (imagine all the dead wallabies and echidnas), it used too much water in a country prone to seasonal droughts, and it represented our self-indulgent greed. We added sugar to our food and sat around and grew fat.

The Shearwater kindergarten was housed in a converted farmhouse surrounded by grass, lemon trees, monkey bars, a sandpit and a cubby house. While Louise's peers at other schools sat fettered to their desks, grappling with pencils and the alphabet, Louise played in the garden, painted watercolour pictures on expensive German paper, stitched a horse of red felt and hand-dyed wool, listened to stories and sang of gnomes going underground (diddly dum).

We walked through the front gate. Around us skipped barefoot children with tousled hair and rainbow clothing. Louise slipped her plump little fingers out of my hand, thrust her schoolbag at me and dashed off to hang upside down from the monkey bars. I left Barbie supervising the chaos of the cloakroom and returned to the veranda. A friend joined me and we watched as another mother sliced fruit for the children's morning tea at a table to our right.

'Riche could tell us the calorie count of those apples and oranges,' I remarked. 'He could probably even tell you the calorie content of an individual grape. The kid has a steel-trap memory.'

'That's odd.' My friend didn't laugh. 'What else is he doing?'

Her gaze fixed on my face and didn't waver while I described the rest of Riche's behaviour: the exercise, the vegetarianism, the haunted look, the weight loss.

'He has anorexia.' My friend sounded unambiguous. And worried. 'I had it years ago. You should take him to a doctor.'

That was all it took—someone to say the word out loud, someone who was smart and knew the illness from personal experience. It meant I wasn't overreacting. And it meant Riche was seriously ill.

My friend continued with a story about a trip to Europe and how eating with her parents in cafes led to her recovery. As she spoke, I thought of what had been happening to Riche. I couldn't point to a time—an hour, a day or a month even—and say that was when the anorexia had started. But the mental changes, the intensity I had noted at the time of the bonfire and the depression associated with the long-running argument with Kevin, they seemed to predate the physical exercise which in turn predated the decreased food intake.

I didn't understand the connections. But I did know I needed to get back to my son, and he needed help. So I said goodbye to my friend and called out to Louise that I was going. Her head spun round towards me.

'Look, Mummy. No hands!'

She stood on top of the monkey bars, one foot planted on each long bar, her arms outstretched. Her cheeks glowed, and she smiled triumphantly. Even from four metres I could see the sparkle in her eyes—huge, like Riche's, but a paler blue—and the tension in her leg muscles as her toes curled over the silver bars. I waved and fought the urge to call, *Don't fall*.

As I drove home, the cows in the paddocks seemed to stare at me with reproach. Poor dumb animals eating their way to the abattoir. I shivered and turned up the heat and tried to anticipate Kevin's response when I told him I thought Riche really did have the plague—in its thoroughly modern and western form.

The cottage creaked and groaned as it settled into the night. My parents and children were in bed and Minnie dozed on the sofa in the loungeroom, her golden body shuddering and twitching. I sat on the front steps, cradled the telephone in my hands and looked at the long, thin shadow I cast on the lawn. Overhead a dusting of stars sparkled against the black sky. I loved it here. These platinum moments when everyone else was in bed. When, if I positioned myself carefully, I could look out and not see another sign of human existence.

But for Kevin the commute was a massive headache, and it was about to get worse. I dialled his number. When he picked up we swapped greetings and then he said he was on another call and would ring back in two minutes. I hung up and stared into the darkness. Ten minutes later, the phone rang.

'Sorry,' Kevin said. 'Client. What's happening?'

I told him about the conversation with my friend. When I'd finished I waited. I heard something in the background. 'Are you typing?'

'Sorry,' Kevin said. 'I have to get this email off.' A pause and a final click. 'Done! Anorexia? Isn't that a girls' disease?'

'Apparently not. Harrison's says it's almost never seen in men. But "almost" must mean that sometimes it is.'

My 1980 edition of Harrison's *Principles of Internal Medicine* had smelled of dust and mould when I took it down and cracked it open. Inside, tucked between obesity and dietary therapy, I found a brief entry on anorexia. Along with vague memories from a psychiatry internship, it now formed the basis of my knowledge.

Kevin sighed. 'What makes you think Riche has it?'

'He's lost weight. He never stops exercising. And he has the right sort of temperament: intelligent, sensitive, high-achieving, competitive.' I didn't mention the controlling and manipulative traits I'd also heard about on the psychiatry ward. They definitely didn't apply to our son. 'It all adds up.'

'Well that's just fucking great.' Kevin paused, and I heard a few more clicks.

'Are you on that damned computer again? This is serious.'

There was a sharp intake of breath at the other end of the telephone and then silence. I imagined Kevin controlling the urge to snap back at me.

Neither of us spoke for a few seconds. A jet engine roared and I pictured oblivious rows of passengers gorging themselves on airplane snacks as they zoomed over my head towards their Gold Coast holidays. Lucky them.

'So,' he said after a while. 'How would he get anorexia?'

And here came the crunch. I wanted there to be a cause for Riche's illness. He couldn't just be the random victim of a hit-and-run fate. Moreover it seemed to me that if we found the cause, we might be able to reverse its effects. There was no logic to this: you lift a car from a man's crushed leg and the man still needs surgery. But I was blindsided in every sense of the word.

My old copy of Harrison's described the illness as a 'disorder of previously healthy adolescent girls who became emaciated as a result of voluntary starvation'. It cited three possible causes. The first was a 'need to break away from a restrictive family environment'. 'Strong mothers' were seen as a particular problem and as far as I knew, here in 2002 this theory still held. The second was depression. The third, 'an abnormality in the satiety centre of the hypothalamus', I promptly disregarded because the author claimed that the evidence for this was 'not persuasive'. That left depression and…well, me. Not looking good. Harrison's was, after all, the authority.

No sooner had I shone the light on myself than I tried to find a way to deflect it. I couldn't bear to think that I might have hurt my son—my beautiful, generous-hearted little boy, with all his earnestness and passion for life—even unintentionally. Kevin, on the other hand, had repeatedly tried to make Riche apologise to his mother just for the sake of peace even though, as far as I could see, Riche had done no wrong. Surely the ongoing stress of that was more likely to have caused Riche's illnesses? Not that Kevin meant to hurt Riche, but we all knew he had the sensitivity of a brick.

And then the thing about strong mothers and anorexic daughters crept back into my mind. Perhaps if strong mothers were a cause of anorexia in daughters, strong fathers might have the same effect on sons. An intra-gender phenomenon. I had never read such a theory but it made sense to me, and I grabbed at it. Of course there was no denying I had made mistakes. But even as I fretted about the influence of the militant diet I had inflicted on my father, I rationalised: I was a first-time offender. Other women talked diets all the time and I didn't see their children fading away. Other mothers moved their children from one town to another, sometimes many moves, and their children didn't starve themselves. As for the 'strong mother' charge that had sent me down this guilt-lined path, well, I definitely held firm opinions. But I wasn't overbearing with my children. I liked to have fun with them. There was no shortage of laughter in our home.

Which left Kevin as the major shareholder in the blame.

Now, with the benefit of the retrospectoscope, I can see it was a way to make sense of a seemingly random situation. But at the time there was the enormous relief of an argument to be had.

'How did he get it?' I snapped. 'That might have something to do with you and your mother.'

Silence. I pictured Kevin in his office on the fifty-sixth floor of the MLC Centre. Most of his colleagues would have gone home but Kevin would be at his desk, surrounded by Perspex deal toys, trophies of a long and successful career, working into the night on a document for some client or other. Was he looking at the computer screen right now? Or staring through the plate glass, mesmerised by the string of lights that looped around Sydney Harbour, while he pondered my accusation? He hated my analytic streak, the way I pored over the minutiae of our lives. And he knew that verbally he was no match for me—a situation, I admitted only to myself, that I tended to exploit. It was my way of redressing the balance in our relationship: of bringing the high-flying businessman who travelled first class and stayed in five-star hotels down to the level of the stay-at-home mother, invisible in her husband's world.

Kevin murmured to himself, an irritated sound. And then, 'What do you mean by that?'

'Riche's fight with your mother. It upset me—and her—for God's sake, it must have been far worse for him. He was only nine and a half. And you tried to bully him into an apology. Do you have any idea what that was like for him?'

'Not this again.'

'Not this again?' What was wrong with my dunderheaded husband? To me at that moment, Kevin's months-long apology campaign looked like a *direct* cause of Riche's illness. And when you did something wrong, you apologised and took your punishment—which in this case would likely be my well-timed reminders of his wrongdoing—before you earned forgiveness.

'So it's my fault?' Kevin let out a long rush of breath; he sounded tired.

'What do you think?' It couldn't be my fault. I was Riche's *mother.*

'I've been an idiot, haven't I?'

I let my silence answer.

'Well, will you take him to see a doctor?'

'Not until I find the right one,' I said. 'It's not as straightforward as you think.'

'He's sick, he sees a doctor. Seems pretty straightforward to me.'

'You don't understand,' I said. 'Most doctors would admit Riche to hospital because they don't know what else to do, and from what I remember hospital programs are punitive. The way they work is, patients earn privileges only if they gain weight—so many kilograms, they let you have a shower. He might have to earn the right to see us or even talk to us by phone. It might take days, maybe even weeks.' I kept picturing Riche in a psychiatry ward full of teenage girls, unable to see us, confined to bed. I was utterly determined both to prevent that and to find a better form of treatment. 'He's *eleven.*'

'If that's what it takes to get him better…'

'But even then it won't necessarily work. This illness can drag on for years. And he still might die.'

There. I'd finally voiced my greatest fear. This wasn't just about a poor appetite; this was a life-threatening illness. Sufferers died in the acute phase, but they also died after being sick for years, sometimes after multiple, and ultimately ineffective, hospital admissions. A ten to twenty percent death rate in all, the highest of any psychiatric illness. Riche could end up a statistic. I shivered. I couldn't let myself think like that. 'There's got to be a better way. I don't know…I read some article in a magazine ages ago about a girl who went overseas for treatment after doctors failed her here. Maybe I can track it down.'

'Well you'd better get cracking. What'll we tell Andy and Louise?'

'The truth. Not much point hiding it.' I wasn't looking forward to those conversations.

'I miss you.' Was there a gap there, between the meaning and the tone of Kevin's words?

'Do you really? You're not going to give up on us?'

This was my dilemma: when I stopped fighting, I felt vulnerable. I felt—I had always felt—I might fail. And the price of failure now was unthinkable.

'I'll never do that.' This time he sounded sincere. 'You're the one who always wants to leave. I'll retire after the next bonus, and we'll all be together.'

'You're coming home for the weekend?'

'Correct. Friday evening. In time for dinner. Don't worry, it'll work out.'

After we'd hung up, I put the telephone down and shifted slightly. The top step was digging into the small of my back. Kevin would leave the decision to me, but I needed him to understand and agree. Hospital was the wrong place for Riche, at least hospital in the form of a months-long admission.

○

Later I tiptoed into my mother's room. She slept alone since her incontinence had driven my father out of her bed and into a transportable cabin I'd found through the second-hand classifieds. It was candy pink and had previously seen service as a down-market brothel. My mother lay on her side, her face to the wall. She looked to be asleep, but when I pulled the sheets up around her shoulders, she turned her head and the left side of her face smiled at me. The muscles on the right remained slack.

'Goodnight, Norma.'

'It's Mandy,' I said. 'Your daughter.'

'So it is. Why are you still here?'

'I live here,' I said. 'Time for you to go to sleep. Sweet dreams.'

I leaned forward, inhaling the mingled scent of talcum powder and urine, and kissed her clammy forehead.

In the next room Louise, sleeping with her eyelids parted to show the whites of her eyes, looked like someone caught between sleep and wakefulness. Andy had thrown off his blankets and sprawled, limbs splayed, with a string of saliva down his chin. Neither child stirred when I switched off the light. I tiptoed across the loungeroom to the study and pushed the door open. A slab of light fell across Riche's face and torso as he lay on his bed. He tossed and turned, moaning softly, and clawed at his sheets with the frantic movements of a frightened animal. I gazed at him for a long moment before I withdrew.

A ndy heard trouble in my voice when I said I needed to talk to
him about Riche.

'Okaaay,' he said, drawing the word out. He put aside his sketch
of a castle and looked at me as if I were the hangman. My palms were
slick with sweat.

'You know how he's been doing all that exercise and not eating
properly?'

A nod. One hand curled tightly around his pencil, the other
beneath his chin. Elbow on the table.

I tightened the noose. 'Dad and I think he might have anorexia.'
Kapow. The hangman kicks the stool. Child sees his future swinging
from the gallows. 'Know what that means?'

'Sort of.' White face. Shallow breaths. The pencil about to snap.

'He's very sick. A voice in his head is telling him he's fat, so he
can't eat. It's not his fault.' I was on the home stretch, breathing more
easily.

Tears streaked Andy's face, lacerating tears. 'How will you get
him better?'

'I don't know. But we will.' I cast around for a less distressing
topic. My eyes lit on his castle drawing, its battlements more serrated

than crenellated. 'That should keep out the Saracens. You'd better finish it.' I kissed him and went to pick up Louise.

My six-year-old daughter, her kindergarten world of felt elephants and cubby houses left behind for the day, sat in the back seat clutching her Barbie backpack and listened to my explanation.

'But he's not even fat.' Her expression, in the rearview mirror, looked puzzled. 'He's skinny.'

'I know,' I said. 'It's weird.'

'Can you play with me when we get home?'

'Not today. Sorry sweetheart, I'm not in the mood for playing games.'

'That's all right,' Louise said. 'I'll play with Andy. And I won't be mean to Riche. What's for afternoon tea?'

And that was that. Or so she thought.

○

If only I could have promised my children that Riche would be right as rain in no time. But now I knew he was sick all I could see was him getting sicker. And I was struggling to understand the nature of the illness myself.

I had only seen it first-hand once, in a girl who was admitted during my three-month psychiatry internship back in the eighties. She fitted the classic picture. Mid-teens, from a privileged family that could afford private school fees, academically gifted and athletic, held a leadership position in the student body. She had the world at her feet and here she was shooting herself in those very same feet by refusing to eat. Her parents were the classic bad guys, heaping pressure on their daughter to live up to their high expectations and controlling her every move like a puppet, an extension of their own thwarted selves.

I listened intently to all the discussions during the medical rounds but never got to speak to the girl. She was out of bounds for a junior doctor like me, a job for the experts. I observed her fishbowl existence from a distance. Watched as her every move was noted. Saw her emaciated body. Heard her agonised wails when the nasogastric tube was inserted into a nostril and pushed down her throat. I felt for her in her isolation.

She frightened me, that girl. How could anyone throw away a golden future like hers? Of course I know now that she was sick, not playing some ghastly game of Russian roulette with her life. She was still there when my rotation finished.

More recently there was the girl in the magazine article. Bronte Cullis, whose name I was yet to recall but who would come to play an important part in our lives. I remembered from the article that Bronte had been in and out of hospital and on nasogastric feeds for a couple of years before her parents, feeling that the Australian medical system didn't have the answers, sent her to a clinic in Canada to save her life. Her mother Jan, the director of the Brisbane clinic where I would soon find myself with Riche, later told me stories about Bronte's hospitalisations. In the end they ran to a predictable schedule: admission to hospital for weight gain followed by discharge, weight loss, readmission. During hospital admissions, Bronte picked up anorexic tricks from fellow patients, ploys such as diluting the nasogastric feed, kinking the tube, or going straight to the source and removing the tube.

Jan often felt as if her daughter was being punished for something beyond her control. One Christmas the staff took away Bronte's books, magazines and access to TV, leaving her with nothing to pass the time until Jan turned up with a book and, despite protests from the staff, read to her daughter.

Bronte's experiences, just a few years before Riche got sick, backed up my own observations. They had left me with two strong impressions of hospital treatment of anorexia: it was brutal, and it didn't work. I also suspected that nothing much had changed, and those suspicions would also prove largely correct. Several years after Riche got sick another girl from Mullumbimby developed anorexia. She landed in Lismore Hospital where, I heard, she was denied phone calls and visits from friends until she put on weight. If there were hospitals available with different practices, they weren't widely advertised.

In time I would come across a form of treatment that supported families caring for sufferers, as long as they were medically stable, in their own homes. But that discovery was months away. I would also come to realise that a twenty-two-year-old copy of Harrison's was not the go-to book for the current state of anorexia treatment. It was, however, all I had at the time. In 2002 we had no internet at the cottage—as a late adopter I was a stranger to the technology anyway—and the nearest serious libraries were in Brisbane, over 150 kilometres away. Despite being out of date, Harrison's wasn't far off the mark with its second and third causes if only I had known it. The 'restrictive family environment' and the 'strong mothers' would prove more contentious.

But for now, I knew nothing of this. It was mostly a mother's instinct that told me that hospital was no place for Riche. I also knew that he was very sick and that hospitalisation was almost inevitable if I took him to a doctor.

The thought terrified me. I knew I had to find a better option.

Kevin's ten-year-old Mercedes Benz pulled up in the carport, its front seat laid back to make room for a surfboard. Kevin got out and threw his wetsuit over the front gate to dry. He stood stretching for a few minutes in the early morning sunshine.

At forty-four Kevin looked strong and muscular, with a surfer's bulging biceps and broad shoulders. His toffee-brown hair was peppered with grey and the chiselled lines of his jaw had softened, but people still routinely assumed he was ten years younger than he was. It was something that never happened to me. Being the older woman in someone's life when in fact you're nineteen months younger is not a good thing. He finished his stretches and came inside, smiling at me.

'You up already?' His voice had the hard, bright edge that meant he was tired and grumpy but determined to put a good face on it. 'I was going to bring you coffee in bed.'

'I couldn't sleep.'

Insomnia had become routine in the two weeks since my friend had said the dreaded A word. I folded a towel and added it to the pile on the table.

Minnie bounded in from the garden and leapt up on Kevin.

'Hey Minnie! Who's a beautiful dog?' Kevin bent down, his lips and eyes squeezed shut, and submitted to a wet and enthusiastic dose of doggy love. 'He's wet.'

'Minnie's a she not a he.' My response was automatic. Three dogs now, all female, and he still couldn't get their gender right. 'Was the surf good?'

'Awesome. The right hander was working at Tallows.' He liked to tell me that surfing relieved his stress, an excuse, I figured, to avoid helping with weekend breakfast duty. I didn't see that his endorphin addiction was the same as my absolute need for a morning coffee. In any case, most days the high seemed to have crashed before he reached our front step. Business Kevin, strung out from work, travel and concern for Riche, was just a few sunburnt cells beneath the determined smiles.

Kevin slid his arms around me from behind. 'Has he eaten?'

'He said he ate two pieces of toast at 5 am. I'm not convinced.'

'What's the deal?' Kevin let go of me. 'He's killing himself. We have to make him eat more.'

'If you hadn't tried to force him to apologise to your mother, he wouldn't be starving himself now.' The minute the words formed, I wanted to take them back. My mother always told me I sounded like a fishwife if I raised my voice. She would have a field day now, if only she had her wits about her. But Kevin's bluster deflated. 'I know. I'm sorry. If I could turn back the clock I would.' He faltered. His voice, when he spoke again, was resigned. 'But I can't, and we have to act.'

'You have a shot at giving him his morning tea then. He wouldn't touch it yesterday. Looked at me like I had a bomb in my hands.'

'All right.' Kevin drew up straight. 'It can't be that hard.'

He went off to the kitchen. Within minutes the smell of grilled cheese on toast wafted through to me and Kevin strode past with a plate, wearing his confidence like an invisible cape. He banged once on Riche's door and marched in.

I put the folded towel on the pile—*lamb to the slaughter*—and waited for the explosion.

'Get that *out* of my room,' Riche shouted loudly enough to be heard across the paddock. 'I told you not to come in here.'

Kevin backed out and shut the door, avoiding eye contact. He took a bite of the cheese toast and handed a piece to Minnie.

'That went well,' I said. 'Any other bright ideas?'

I knew how I sounded, and I couldn't help myself. Kevin had a way of dropping in on the middle of a situation, certain of the solution—a habit detected by the children as well. One weekend Louise stood hands on hips, belly thrust forward, and said to him, 'You might be the boss of Merrill Lynch, but you're not the boss of the family.'

Now he licked his lips and said, 'You're the doctor.'

Good point. I was, but it wasn't helping. Six years of government-funded training down the gurgler. What did you do if a child simply refused to eat?

'Should I shove the cheese toastie in his mouth and sit on him?' Kevin said, only half joking.

I'd read about French farmers stuffing food into geese with wooden poles to fatten them up for pate de foie gras. I fantasised, briefly, about doing this to Riche then shook my head. 'Even if we forced food into his mouth, we can't force him to swallow,' I said. 'Besides, if we push him too hard, we might make him worse.'

I was thinking about the great red herring of anorexia, the issue of control. I'd been taught as a student that when teenage girls felt themselves to be overly controlled by their parents, they chose to control the one thing in their lives they could: the amount they ate. This belief was common among the general population too. I didn't actually believe Riche was consciously choosing to starve himself, though. In fact his anorexia seemed to be about loss of control. Sure, early on he'd chosen to become a vegetarian but at some point the situation had changed. Having observed his gradual descent into illness (a phase not generally seen by doctors and psychologists), I understood that Riche was now unable to control the voice in his head that was telling him he was fat. Any behaviour of his that seemed controlling was a direct result of his delusional thinking: he needed to control his environment, which included his family, in order to keep the terrifying threat of calories at bay.

At the same time as I thought this, and this is where my thinking got confused, I wondered if he had developed the illness as an *unconscious* (and therefore blameless) means of control in response to his control-freak parents. If this were the case, surely forcing him to eat would exacerbate the problem—a conclusion I now view as the cognitive equivalent of the atheist who kneels down and prays when there's a crisis. Just in case.

'He'll die if we don't do something.' Kevin picked up the last piece of toasted cheese. 'Want a bite?'

I shook my head. *He will die.* He could. It was true. Between ten and twenty percent: the figures silently paraded in my mind. But instead of motivating me, these statistics and Kevin's words simply whipped my brain up into a neural storm that left me unable to think.

The bedroom door opened and Riche came out, a malevolent, ghost-like figure. He made his way to his sandals by the front door, each step slow and cautious as if the floor might open up and swallow him. Then he slipped his feet into his sandals, not bothering to pull the straps up behind his ankles. Without a word, he set off on another calorie-burning mission.

'Did you see that?' I said. 'That habit started in the last day or so. He won't touch his sandal straps. I wonder why.'

'He's mad.' Kevin raised his hands in a gesture of defeat. 'He's committing a slow form of suicide.'

'He doesn't realise he's killing himself.' I was sure of that, at any rate. 'He just thinks he's losing some excess flab.'

'Well you'd better come up with answers soon. He's not going to snap out of it.' Kevin shut the dishwasher. 'I'll be cleaning the chook house if you need me.'

○

Kevin had always deferred to me when it came to decisions about the children, starting with when to conceive them. From then on we had a clear but unspoken demarcation of duties. Kevin was the breadwinner. He had the stellar career and the drive. I decided that one high-powered career in the family was enough and gave up my medical career, which I had never enjoyed, to become a stay-at-home mother.

Even when we lived in Sydney Kevin didn't see much of the kids until weekends. He left for work before they woke and returned after bedtime. He travelled, often for weeks at a time, to the US or Europe. When he reappeared, he'd bring the latest Barbie doll and Pokémon character from either FAO Schwartz in New York or, more often, from the boot of my car. I'd pick the toys up at the local Toys-R-Us and leave them for Kevin to collect on his way to the front door. While Kevin met with corporate kings, I selected schools, bought Fred Bare clothing in small sizes and ordered jumping castles for birthday parties. While I dabbed calamine lotion on chicken pox, Kevin watched from the doorway with a mobile phone to his ear. So I was neither surprised nor displeased that he waited for me to come up with the answers to this latest crisis. It was what we both knew.

He was right, though. Riche wasn't going to snap out of it. I needed to find a solution. And I still thought the solution was likely to be found in the cause. I probably thought it was a bit like plumbing. Remove the blockage, fix the leak and hey presto: pipe fixed.

In the meantime, I wished I could find a compliant doctor who would admit Riche to hospital for a week or two—for intravenous rehydration and nasogastric feeding to stabilise him—while I figured out the next step. As far as I knew, that option didn't exist in Australia. It was all-or-nothing: Riche could have outpatient psychotherapy, or the medical establishment would step in with a non-negotiable package of weeks, or even months, of hospitalisation with all that entailed.

○

The soles of Riche's unfastened sandals slapped against the wooden floor of the loungeroom. He was panting, and sweat shone on his face—deathly pale despite an hour-long walk in the heat. Mid-October and already the mercury was climbing. We were in for a scorcher of a summer.

'You look hot,' I said. 'Have some water. You're not drinking enough.'

'I'm not thirsty,' Riche said. 'I drank several glasses of water before you got up.'

This didn't ring true to me, but I didn't know what to do. So I prepared a small bowl of spinach and ricotta ravioli for his lunch and took it to him. He put down his comic and looked up at me from his futon.

'Want to go to circus training this afternoon?' I said.

Even as I asked, I knew this was a bad idea, but the small part of me not looking for metaphorical blockages or leaks clung desperately to the hope that engaging in social activity would jolt him out of his 'slump'.

'It's too hot. I think I'll stay home.' He wriggled while he spoke and looked away, so I got the sense this wasn't the real reason.

Ten minutes later he disappeared down the rainforest trail despite the blazing sun, leaving his lunch half eaten on the floor. After this walk, he made straight for the bathroom. The sound of running water was followed by the creak of the linen cupboard door. I went in to check on him, wrinkling my nose at the smell of my mother's nappies. Riche was drying his hands on a towel in the cupboard.

'That's disgusting,' I said, 'and it makes more work for me. What's wrong with the towel by the basin?' Our ship might be sinking, but by God it was going down with an orderly linen cupboard.

'It's dirty. Other people use it.' Riche spoke in a monotone, his eyes downcast. When he had finished, he kicked the cupboard door shut. Then he eased his way out sideways, for some reason taking care to avoid contact with either the wall or me.

○

My father made the obvious suggestion that I weigh Riche. We didn't own a set of scales: until recently, body weight had not been an issue in our household. But weighing Riche seemed like a good idea, so I went shopping. I put the new scales centre-stage in front of the diningroom fireplace.

When Riche came in from his walk, I cornered him and pointed to the scales. 'Hop on.'

He did; in fact, he seemed pleased to obey me.

I looked over his shoulder at the dial. 'Twenty-five kilograms!' I felt sick. 'You've lost four kilograms in eight weeks. Louise weighs almost as much and she's five years younger. What the hell is going on? Don't you see you need to eat?'

'I do eat. Stop nagging. I'm going for a walk.' Riche got off the scales, steel in his eyes, and headed for the door.

○

Kevin and I fell into circular arguments that started with the question, 'Why don't you take him to see a doctor?' and ended with, 'You don't understand.' Or, 'It's your fault.'

During one particular top-step summit, a variation emerged.

'Maybe he's sick because you moved him up here to Byron,' Kevin said. 'The place is full of vegetarians and people on strange diets. Ever consider that?'

I studied a chewed hibiscus leaf. Kevin was right about diets and

Byron Bay. It was not only a Mecca for vegetarians; it was the gluten-free capital of Australia. Then there were the people who ate according to their blood group—type A and you need red meat, type O and you don't, or perhaps it was the other way around. Not to mention the macrobiotics, organics and biodynamics. If you wanted to obsess about your diet, this was the place to do it.

'Don't be stupid,' I said. No way was I letting him off the hook. 'You're looking for excuses.'

Truth was, though I let Kevin believe I thought it was his fault, in secret I had my hard hat strapped on and was continuing to excavate our past for anything either of us might have done, or Riche might have experienced, that had resulted in his illness. And I was finding that no hard hat could protect me from the pain of thinking my name was on that list. The local predilection for dietary obsession linked straight back to my impulsive move north, and the diet I'd foisted on my father was taking on a more sinister hue. Kevin was looking less and less like the major shareholder when it came to blame. And the knowledge was eating away at me.

○

One evening Kevin suggested we walk the dogs down our rainforest trail. We wandered silently under the leafy canopy of strangler figs, firewheels and bangalow palms. Staghorns dripped from overhanging branches and the rich scent of rotting plant matter filled the air. Kevin pointed at a thin red line of exposed volcanic soil that cut through the native grass on our rainforest trail. 'He walks in exactly the same place each time. Bizarre, isn't it?'

I placed a foot on the line and followed it for a few metres, then stepped back on to the grass. 'Goodness knows what's going on in his head.' My beautiful open child had become secretive. If I were to ask him to explain his behaviour, he would look at me as if I were trying to extract state secrets.

Kevin bent to pull a handful of crofton, a weed. 'You really think I caused Riche's illness, don't you?'

'Partly,' I said, although I was beginning to wonder why an argument would cause my son to starve himself where another child might simply sulk in the corner for an hour. 'You and your mother. It's too much of a coincidence.'

'I'll tell him I'm sorry.'

I put my arms around Kevin and hugged him, resting my head against his muscular chest as I breathed in the salt-washed scent of his body. We'd shared nineteen years of the unexpected pleasures and small betrayals that come with married life, and in all that time Kevin had stood by me, his eyes fixed on the vision of us. I thought about the possibility that our marriage would fail with Riche's illness, and knew in my heart that if it did it would be me doing the leaving.

Back at the cottage, Kevin knocked on Riche's door and went in. I waited nearby, straining to hear their conversation.

'Listen mate, I'm sorry.' Kevin sounded awkward. 'I shouldn't have asked you to apologise to my mother. It wasn't your fault.'

'You're only saying that because Mum told you to.' Riche's voice was loud and angry. 'You don't mean it. Get out.'

Kevin closed the door, puckered his lips and blew out hard. Then he stepped towards me and spoke, his voice low. 'Maybe it'd help if I got my mother to apologise.' I gave him a grateful look, aware of how much he would dread such a call.

He took his BlackBerry—his blessed BlackBerry—out to the veranda. When he came back in, he looked hopeful and a bit relieved.

'Mum wasn't home.' He wound the cord of the earpiece around the BlackBerry and put it on the mantelpiece. 'I spoke to Dad. He said they're adults so they should be big enough to apologise.'

There it was again—a stupid expression relating morality to size. It seemed like something that shouldn't be said in the vicinity of someone who thought he was too big. Nonetheless, I appreciated

Kevin's effort. I was grateful to his father too, and held out high hopes that an apology from my mother-in-law would make a difference.

○

A week later my father came back from our mailbox waving a small white envelope postmarked Perth and addressed to Riche, who tore it open and read swiftly.

'It's from Nana. She says, *I'm sorry you were upset that we didn't see eye-to-eye on some things.*' He looked up, glowering. 'That's not an apology.'

I silently agreed. Riche crumpled the paper, threw it on the table, and went to his bedroom. He tried to kick the door shut but over-balanced and nearly fell.

'Why don't you use your hands?' I said.

'It's easier this way.' Riche steadied himself and kicked again. This time the door shut.

A short time later he emerged, slid his feet into his sandals and went out the front door. His exercise routine had changed over the past few weeks. He'd given up circus, martial arts and athletics and had abandoned push-ups and cartwheels in favour of rainforest walks—for up to five hours a day. He never ventured off our property.

When he returned he kicked his sandals off—still no-hands—and got on the scales. He stared at the dial as if in a trance then went to his room. By now he did this five, six, even seven times a day. Paralysed by fear, I was unable to make the simple decision to put the scales away.

But paralysis didn't stop me from realising that my theory about effecting a cure by removing the cause was flawed. I'd hung my hopes on the power of Kevin and his mother's apologies, but they'd made no difference. The solution was not to be found in simply fixing the cause, just as repairing a leaky pipe would not take care of water damage. Which was also, I decided, why psychotherapy alone would fail to add an ounce of fat to my son.

It was more food he needed right now, not an archaeological dig. The question was: how to get that food into him?

To do list

1) Ring therapist recommended by coffee shop woman.

2) Pay accounts.

3) Organise car registration.

4) Cancel hairdresser.

Who had time for blonde foils? I took a glass of wine out to the top step at the front of the cottage to consider the first item on my list, even though I knew I should be making the most of Riche's walk to get dinner ready. He had taken to supervising meal preparation. He hovered behind me, his arms rigidly at his sides to avoid contact with anything, his head bowed, his hair, almost reaching his shoulders, falling forward, half-concealing the scowl on his face.

Despite his thin and fragile appearance his force of will was strong, almost a vibration in the air around him, so much so that a lot of the time I tended to stop seeing his thinness. Being around Riche was like being tailed by a police car, lights and siren poised for the first sign of an infringement. This achieved his objective admirably. It was impossible to sneak extra calories in the form of oil or butter into anything I cooked. I'd wondered if it would be best to ban him from the kitchen—but mightn't that just make him more anxious? Until I'd found evidence one way or another, I'd decided to avoid the issue and cook in his absence. So I needed to go inside. But first the matter of the coffee shop woman's therapist.

So far I had not sought professional help. I hadn't been able to track down any eating-disorder experts in the area and I was determined to keep Riche out of hospital. Nasogastric tubes, long admissions, punitive-style treatment: I didn't want to put my son through this. But I knew I had to act soon. I knew I should already have acted.

My opinion about what action to take, however, was about as firm as Riche's tofu. I was pretty sure that taking the therapy route to find the cause of his illness would make not a scrap of difference, but I wasn't ready to resort to the only other option I had at this point—the local doctor. Riche's current condition made it more likely than ever that a doctor would admit him to hospital, where he might well end up like the magazine girl. Which took us back to therapists. Perhaps my underlying assumption was wrong; maybe instead of looking for causes, a therapist would help Riche conquer his fear of fat. A preemptive strike rather than a historical study.

Then again, my coffee shop woman made good coffee, but did that qualify her to recommend a therapist for my son? Therapists are as common as coffee shops in the Byron Shire and, like the coffee, their standard is variable. Anyone can take a counselling course, tack up their shingle, light a few candles, burn some incense and they're in business. Cash only.

Not for my son. I wanted someone with proper qualifications.

The Yellow Pages weren't much help. None of the therapists advertised a special interest in eating disorders. Perhaps Riche's illness was a Family Problem or an Unresolved Childhood Issue. Or did eating disorders come under the umbrella of Women's Issues? These days, with almost everyone connected to the internet and a good, if short, list of evidence-based treatment providers to refer to, there is useful information easily available, but we were a few years away from that and I was relying on word of mouth. To date, nothing had come of several leads.

Now, when I dust off my retrospectoscope to view that solitary figure with her faithful chardonnay, I wonder what the hell she's waiting for. That woman knew anorexia was a potentially life-threatening illness. She knew prompt and aggressive treatment achieved the best results. She knew her son was deteriorating. And still she dithered on the top step.

She frustrates me, but I resist the urge to take a cattle prod to her back. I remind myself that when she looked at her mother she had ample reason to be wary of medical intervention. And I remind myself that, although the need for immediate help was obvious, she knew her son better than anyone. Her knowledge made it quite obvious to her that long periods of hospitalised isolation would not be the help he needed. Perhaps more importantly, she knew it was not the help *she* needed to assist her son's recovery.

○

I put my empty wine glass on the sink and got to work peeling potatoes. While they were bubbling in the pan I unwrapped the swordfish fillets and laid them on the chopping board. Next I mixed thyme, black pepper, dry mustard, oregano, cayenne pepper and a generous shake of sweet paprika. I checked to make sure Riche hadn't returned before I quickly brushed olive oil—lovely calorie-dense olive oil—over the fillets, my pulse all the time thudding in my ears. Then I started to press the Cajun mix into the pale flesh. I had nearly finished when I heard Riche's voice from behind me.

'Those pieces of fish are huge. Don't expect me to eat that much.'

My throat closed but I ignored him. We could fight over quantities later. Riche followed me to the oven and watched as I slid the tray of fish in. Then he disappeared into the bathroom. The fish sizzled and the aroma of spices filled the room. When the potatoes were ready, I mashed them.

'Don't use milk or butter.' Riche's voice, loud and sullen, came from behind.

I jumped and looked round to see his eyes fixed on me. 'Of course not.' I hit the masher hard against the side of the saucepan to dislodge the potato clumps and looked back at my son.

He shook his hands, spraying water droplets over the floor, his gaze still fixed on me. Suddenly he turned and went back into the bathroom to wash his hands again and this time I furtively dropped in a pat of butter. I wondered if it was the right thing to do. Basic as it seemed, the decision wasn't easy. Under Riche's gaze a potato felt like a grenade in my hand.

Riche returned to the kitchen, the wet skin on the backs of his hands red and cracked. 'You didn't put anything in the mashed potato, did you?' His voice quivered with fear.

'No.'

I had always prided myself on my honesty.

Riche ate in the loungeroom; the rest of us crowded around the long wooden table in the dining area. I tried to relax and enjoy the fish, thinking all the time of Riche tasting the butter in the potato.

My mother looked across at Louise. 'That little girl needs to have her hair brushed, Norma.'

Take a breath. Be patient. She can't help it.

'Norma's your sister. I'm your daughter.' I nodded my head towards Louise. 'And that's your granddaughter.'

'Really?' My mother's eyebrows arched in surprise. She beamed at Louise, who smiled encouragingly. 'Well isn't that nice!'

Louise looked over to the loungeroom table. 'Riche just got up,' she said in a loud whisper. She leaned to her left to get a better look, then turned back to me, her face solemn. 'I don't think he finished his fish.'

The slam of Riche's door put an end to further conversation. Later, when I went to collect his plate, I saw that Louise was right. He'd eaten only half of his fish. The potato was untouched.

○

Andy's eyes were bright with tears at bedtime.

'Riche said he hates me. He said to stay away from him.'

'He doesn't mean it.' I sat on Andy's bed and hugged him, feeling utterly defeated. 'He's sick, and it makes him say mean things.'

'I know, but he's my best friend.' It was true. I thought of all the photos I had of them, usually the two brothers side by side, faces beaming, Riche's arm slung around Andy's shoulders which were, right now, shaking beneath my hands. Tears streamed down his face and he looked up at me. 'Louise plays baby games.'

I pulled him closer and nuzzled the top of his head. 'You'll get him back. I promise.'

'Will you read to me?'

I was about to make an excuse—I'm too tired, I need to get Riche to eat more, I have to talk to Dad—but his pleading look stopped me.

'One chapter, okay?'

○

The coffee shop woman's therapist didn't answer my call. Someone told me she was taking a break. I followed up a few more leads: a therapist in Ocean Shores, one in Mullumbimby, to no avail. In a desperate moment, I even considered a sand therapist until I realised Riche wouldn't touch the sand because it wasn't sterile. Faced with these dead ends I paid my accounts and car registration, ignored my grey regrowth, sipped chardonnay on the top step and hoped Riche would improve. Looking back, I see I had my head buried deep in the red volcanic sand.

○

There was one hot day when I watched as Riche returned from the trail in his trance-like state. At the diningroom doorway he caught sight of a crumb-covered plate on the table and flinched. He took two small sideways steps, keeping his gaze fixed on the plate as if it were about to explode. Mystified, I kept watching. Riche seemed unaware of my presence. He took a third step sideways, to the bathroom door. Then he turned and ducked into the bathroom. He repeated the whole process in reverse when he came out. Thus a new habit was born. It was like flicking a switch.

At first I rolled my eyes. He had to be pulling our legs on this one, right? But he stuck to the ritual every single time he went to the bathroom and gradually it dawned on me: Riche was scared he would get fat if he went near the kitchen or the diningroom table. He seemed to think that calories could travel through the air and penetrate his skin like a miniature marauding army.

Suddenly, his habit of drying his hands on a clean towel in the cupboard made sense. He must think the rest of the family left calories on the shared handtowel. Doorknobs, sandal straps, the kitchen itself: lingering calories clustered and seethed on these things. It explained why, in the last few weeks, he had given up supervising my cooking. It explained why he followed the exact same path—a trusted, calorie-free path—each time he walked in the rainforest. It explained why he was unable to let a hairdresser touch his hair. And it frightened me to realise that a boy who was intelligent enough to win an academic scholarship at the age of eight could think this way. His ability to make sense in every other aspect of life made his behaviour seem even more grotesque.

○

I thought these latest, frightening symptoms might settle if I rid the house of meat. I threw out packets of bacon and ham, a neatly wrapped parcel of sausages, mince for the dogs—steamed fish would bring a shine to their coats—and my father's tins of baked beans with sausages.

'Isn't that extreme?' Kevin asked.

'No,' I said, although the only thing I remained sure of was my decision to keep Riche out of hospital.

One meat-free week made no difference to Riche, but with no other solution in sight, I kept at it like a madwoman. For the most part Riche remained quarantined in his room or continued his walk towards weightless perfection in the rainforest. But the pattern of his walks changed, becoming shorter and more frequent. He came in one day, looking pale and shaky. I checked the wall thermometer.

'It's thirty-six degrees, Riche. Have some water or you'll dehydrate.'

'I had some earlier,' he said, his averted eyes giving away the lie. As far as I could tell, Riche drank water only once each day, in the late afternoon. He used the same glass each time, a seven-ounce Vegemite jar.

Boy goes to his bedroom. Door slams shut. Mother is left perplexed.

Later I stood in the doorway to Riche's room and watched as he slept, his face turned towards the door. Above his futon, a hand-written note was taped to the wall beneath the window. It had been there a few weeks, and the edges were starting to curl. In the dim light, I couldn't make out the writing but knew the words by heart:

Breakfast: 2 slices of toast—plain
Morning tea: 1 slice of raisin toast—plain
Lunch: small serve of spinach and ricotta ravioli—plain
Dinner: something

I crept in and knelt by his side, frightened by the pallor of his skin, an almost translucent white. His lips were peeling, and his chest rose in rapid, shallow bursts. He reminded me of the baby birds we had cared for, with their bony wings and fragile legs. I wanted to scoop him up and hold him in my arms. That would wake him so I stroked his arm. A stick insect arm, a coffin arm. I lifted his hand and pressed my fingers to the inside of his wrist where the skin was cold and dry. I felt the slow, hesitant beat of his pulse: forty-eight beats per minute. For a brief deluded moment, I wondered if this reflected his cardiac fitness from all that exercise. But then I realised the slow rate was more likely a survival mechanism, his body's attempt to conserve energy. And it might also be a sign of damage to his heart muscle. I gently returned his arm to his side and pulled the sheet up under his chin. I had to find help soon. Time was running out.

Riche was refusing to get out of the car, this child who, although spirited, had always been reasonably obedient.

I got out and walked around to open his door—the car door handle was the most recent object to joint the ranks of the unclean. 'Either you go in or the doctor comes to you,' I said. Riche glared at me, got out and walked off, leaving me to shut the door. I could almost feel the turbulence in his wake as I followed him. Inside, I checked in with the receptionist and took a seat. Riche looked searchingly at the seat next to me, and hesitated but eventually sat down. He jiggled his legs. I resisted the urge to lay a hand on them.

I had been given the name of a woman whose daughter had anorexia. Finally—someone who knew the treatment terrain. But my excitement faded when I spoke to her. She had been unable to find successful treatment for her daughter locally. The girl was still sick after five years and several long hospital admissions, including a stay in intensive care—the outcome I would go to any lengths to prevent. Still, the woman gave me the name of a clinic in Brisbane, 150 kilometres away, that specialised in eating disorders. It was Footprints of Angels. The original Footprints of Angels in Melbourne hadn't worked out for her daughter, but the woman thought it might be different for us.

The distance would cause significant family disruption, so first I wanted to try this doctor, whom someone else had recommended as being good with kids, in a town considerably closer to home. It was a long shot. Odds were on he'd have learned the same theories on cause and treatment of anorexia as I did in medical school, approaches a day-to-day familiarity with the illness had led me to believe were wrong. But this was it: I had no other local options, so I'd made the appointment.

A cranky-looking doctor in a tailored suit came down the corridor and spoke to the receptionist. The doctor picked up a file and called Riche's name. We followed him into his office.

'Take a seat.' Not even the ghost of a smile. 'What seems to be the problem?'

Riche sat on the edge of a seat, his lips clamped together.

'Riche's not eating,' I said.

'Mum serves dinner too late,' Riche said. 'I'm too tired to eat.'

I gripped the seat of my chair and sat forward. 'That's not fair Riche. That was back when I took you to all the after-school activities. These days I get dinner on the table between six and six-thirty.'

The doctor looked at me. 'There's no point arguing about that sort of thing,' he said, his voice stern. 'It is important for you to have dinner ready on time.'

I sank back into my seat. This was not what I had expected. Had the doctor ever sat through a meal with someone who approached food like a conscientious objector? And if he wanted to lay down the law regarding my parenting, shouldn't he do it privately? It was hard enough getting Riche to cooperate without being undermined in front of him.

'What else has been happening?'

'Riche's become a vegetarian,' I said. 'It's quite extreme; he won't go anywhere near meat. It's as if he thinks it will contaminate him.'

The doctor made notes.

'And he even seems paranoid about water.'

Raised eyebrows and more note-taking. The doctor looked up. 'I want to weigh you, Riche.'

Riche leapt to his feet. *Now you're talking.* He kicked his sandals off and stepped onto the scales. Flicking his hair out of his eyes, he peered at the needle. It swung to twenty-five kilograms. The doctor noted the weight on Riche's file and then looked at me.

'I'm not making a diagnosis yet, but I'm sending you to a dietician.' A few more notes. 'And I want you to make an appointment with a psychologist.'

That was it? The doctor should have been able to make the diagnosis on the history I'd given. Instead he was sending us to a dietician, presumably for a meal plan, although he didn't have the courtesy to explain that. Nothing wrong with meal plans, but what I needed was for Riche to execute those plans. The dietician was unlikely to help me with that. More worryingly, the doctor was sending us to a psychologist who would probably want to go searching for causes. And I'd already discovered what a time-waster that was. Meanwhile my son was getting sicker by the day.

I sat forward again, clutching my bag, anxious to leave as the doctor wrote out the referrals, placed them in envelopes, sealed the envelopes and gave them to me. I felt my fingers itch. As a resident medical officer at the Royal Children's Hospital in Melbourne, I'd learned as an article of faith: *Always listen to the parents; always include the parents.* Now I was a parent and nobody, but nobody, sealed documents relating to my child. I wasn't a war criminal, I was a mother. I needed to know what was going on.

'Here are the referrals. I'll see Riche again in a week.'

Back in the car, I tore open the envelope addressed to the dietician. The note said:

Thank you for seeing Richard, who has recently become a vegetarian and finds meat disgusting. He and his mother need to be clear on his calorie intake. I will see him weekly until the psychologist has assessed if outpatient management is possible.

I screwed it up and threw it over my shoulder into the rising tide of rubbish in the back. Clear on his intake? If Riche got any clearer on that he would become completely transparent. The problem was how to make him *eat* the required calories. The other problem was that I had brought along a child with a known history of starvation and refusal of fluids, and the doctor hadn't even looked in his mouth to see if his tongue was dry or checked for a postural drop in his blood pressure (a decrease in blood pressure on standing after lying down)—both signs of dehydration. Nor had the doctor ordered any blood or urine tests to make sure starvation and dehydration had not caused dangerous electrolyte imbalances or organ damage.

In some ways this worked in my favour—I didn't want Riche admitted to hospital. But it revealed the direction of the doctor's thinking, and I was beginning to understand even then (although it would become clearer from information I came across much, much later) that it was fundamentally flawed. He was going to base his decision about any hospital admission on a psychological assessment, when it should have been a medical decision, based on Riche's physical condition.

That doctor had seen the last of Riche and me. The dietician was based at a hospital, making him guilty by association, and in any case I didn't see how he would help.

Which left the psychologist. The referral was a bland 'Please assess'. All right, I thought, simmering down. Where was the harm? For reasons that still remain unclear to me, I thought that perhaps the psychologist would tell me how to get Riche to eat. I decided to make an appointment.

The psychologist presented in I'm-your-friend casual attire and greeted us with a smile. She made a few disarming remarks and adopted an empathetic expression while I told my story. When I finished, there was a momentary pause. I waited for the expression to translate to words of help, or at least comfort.

○

The psychologist studied the page and looked up. 'Do you think you are triangulating in a relationship with Kevin and Riche?'

Triangulating?

Twenty minutes with us and this psychologist turns our family into mathematical psychobabble. Did she really think my interference in Kevin and Riche's argument was causing Riche to stop eating? Was she saying that I was too *controlling*? It seemed we were fair and square back in the land of cause, which I'd been trying so hard to get beyond, and of which I was, apparently, a registered citizen.

'I think Riche wants space to sort things out with his father without you.' She swivelled her chair to face Riche. 'Is that right?'

Riche nodded. A sucker punch. It was hard not to feel betrayed by his dismissal of the weeks, months even, when I'd sat back and watched, trying not to intervene, as he and Kevin fought with one another. I reminded myself that Riche was a child, a sick one, and focused my anger on the woman behind the desk with the cookie-cutter solutions. Well, she could try to fit me into the shape of the dysfunctional mother in her seventies textbooks. But if she thought this kind of discussion was going to get Riche eating, she needed to think again.

'Old people can get stuck in their ways,' she was saying to Riche. 'You have to cut your nana some slack, and you have to realise your dad's relationship with his mother is important.'

The kid was starving himself to death and this woman was advocating the cutting of some slack. I leaned back and said a few mental oms.

When the hour was up the psychologist stood, her veneer of friendliness back in place as she reached out to shake my hand. 'Why don't you take a few hours off?' she said. 'Go shopping. Go out to lunch. Give Riche and Kevin some time to sort themselves out.'

Jerk, I thought. 'Great,' I said. I shook her hand, and we left.

'The psychologist doesn't understand,' Riche said as we drove home.

'She doesn't know what she's talking about,' I agreed. 'We won't go back to her.'

'She's taking Dad's side because he's an adult.' Riche's voice was small and lost-sounding. 'I know Nana's important to Dad. She's more important to him than I am.'

I could see it would appear that way to Riche. I bit my lip. 'That's not true. He just doesn't want to fight with her.'

○

It was clear that after two attempts I had run out of local options. I would ring Footprints of Angels and talk to Jan Cullis. Jan wasn't a doctor; she was an educational psychologist. The techniques she embraced were considered 'non-standard' in the medical profession, but her daughter Bronte had spent years fighting anorexia in a Canadian clinic after the Australian system failed her. She might understand the illness. It was worth a shot.

In the meantime, I was absolutely beat. Maybe I would take tomorrow off. Just in case the psychologist was on the money with the triangulating. Surely no harm could come of leaving Riche with Kevin for just one day. It might even do some good.

So I spent a pleasant day cruising the antique stores, gift shops and boutiques in Bangalow in the Byron Bay hinterland. The sun hung low over the Nightcap Ranges as I drove home humming to myself. I pulled into the carport, pleased to see Andy running across the front lawn—pleased until I got out of the car and from a distance of three metres saw the look on his face.

'I'm so glad you're back.' He paused to catch his breath. 'Riche and Dad have been fighting.'

I hurried across the lawn to Andy and put a hand on his shoulder. 'What happened?'

Andy looked like he might cry. He said Kevin had asked to join Riche on his walk. Riche had said no, so Kevin had followed him down the rainforest trail, keeping ten paces behind.

'Riche started yelling at Dad.' Andy was stuttering in his haste to tell the story. 'I could hear him from the sandpit. He said, "You don't fucking understand."'

'Riche swore at Dad?' I'd never heard Riche swear.

Andy nodded. 'Dad asked Riche to help him understand.'

Kevin had used, according to Andy, his 'chuckling voice', a voice edged with subversive laughter. A voice well known to the family. It had taken me years to understand that it was a tic, that the hint of laughter betrayed not ridicule but Kevin's discomfort with emotions.

'Riche got madder and ran off.' Andy had tears in his eyes. 'And Dad asked me what his problem was.'

I found Kevin sitting at the table on the veranda talking on his BlackBerry. I made hang-it-up signs and pulled out a chair. Kevin held up a finger.

'Gotta go, mate.' A pause. 'Correct. Fax it to me and I'll call you when I've read it.' He hit a button on the BlackBerry, pulled the earplug out and wound up the cord. Ritual completed, he gave me a flashbulb smile. 'Another deal. How was your day?'

I leaned forward and put my hands on the table; my mother would have said I was on the warpath. 'What did you do to Riche?'

The smile disappeared. 'Yeah, good to see you too.'

'Can't I even go out for a few hours without you and Riche fighting?'

'You told me to watch him. I asked him if I could keep him company while he walked. He said no. I thought he might collapse on the trail, so I followed him.'

It was a hot day. Kevin's concerns were right on target.

'You're right.' I felt slightly ashamed. 'I did ask you.'

The day had proven one thing for sure: the psychologist had grossly underestimated the extent of the discord between Riche and

Kevin. It was going to take more than my absence for father and son to 'sort themselves out'. Even if they did, Riche seemed unlikely to line up for a celebratory feast any time soon.

I found Riche in the rainforest.

'I hear you had a fight with Dad.'

Riche looked at me, his eyes obsidian chips in a face of chalk. 'Keep him away from me.'

'I won't leave you with him again,' I said.

The rhythm of walking soothed me. Riche followed the thin red line; I kept to the grass, making sure to leave a buffer zone between us. We didn't speak but I hoped my presence was some comfort. Fifty metres along, the trail widened to form a circle of grass at the end of the ridge, an area we called the Point. We were closer to the ocean here and the sound of the waves drowned out highway noise. This was one of my favourite areas of the property. To the right a stand of mature cordylines framed a view of Simpson's Creek. Beyond was Tyagerah Nature Reserve and the contour of the coastline, a gentle curve towards Byron Bay with a view of white-capped breakers rolling in from the open water.

'Beautiful, isn't it?'

Riche nodded. 'I want to live in the bush.' His expression softened and the tension drained from his body. For a moment I caught a glimpse of the old Riche, the idealistic, nature-loving boy. 'I wouldn't need much—just a few books and a blanket. I'd forage for food.'

'I've something to tell you.' I felt like a traitor, any sense of peace shattered. I wanted to wrap Riche in a blanket, bundle him into the car and disappear with him into the bush, away from this suffering— not deliver the news that I was taking him to Brisbane for treatment. Taking him away, for days at a time, from his beloved rainforest trail. At least I assumed he still loved it. Maybe it had become merely an obsession, a penance perhaps, something his mind was forcing him to do to compensate for his meagre intake even when he felt on the verge of collapse.

Riche's face mirrored my serious tone. The tension returned to his body. 'What?'

I told him about the clinic, emphasised its compassionate approach to treating the illness that he didn't believe he had. Riche started pacing in front of me, taking small jerky steps, while I spoke.

'It's an outpatient clinic.' I tried to resurrect an aura of calm, kept my tone even. 'We'll live at home.'

'It's not a trick, is it?' Riche stopped and searched my face for signs of deception. He was a mass of twitches, looked like a frightened rabbit about to dart off through the cordylines. 'Promise me you won't put me in hospital.'

'Come with me to the clinic, and I promise I won't put you in hospital.'

'Okay,' he said in a low, frightened voice.

I had to strain my eyes to make out his thin red line as we headed back to the cottage in the dusk, but Riche seemed to have no trouble. Completely clear to me was my commitment to Riche.

I had given my word, and it was my bond. I had that, at least, in common with the financial world of my husband.

A classic case, Jan said. Five or more years. We had left Footprints of Angels after our initial interview and were back in our hotel room. I had chosen a hotel with room service since Riche would never set foot in a restaurant. I held out the menu for him to read and suggested as an inducement a post-dinner visit to Games Workshop. It had been a much-loved treat when we lived in Sydney and I knew there was a branch here in Brisbane too.

Riche read the menu from a distance of a metre. 'There's nothing vegetarian.' He retreated to his side of the room.

I checked. The vegetarian options were limited but they did exist. I chose one of the 'healthy' low-fat options marked with an asterisk; Riche might be more likely to eat that. I still didn't realise that I was playing into the hands of an illness that is the greatest limbo dancer of all time: lower the bar and it will simply lower it further.

Riche's fruit plate and plain pasta—no oil, no cheese—arrived a short time later, along with my inoffensive vegetarian lasagna. Riche remained standing to eat two pasta spirals. The rest he pushed under a lettuce leaf. Next he picked up a slice of apple and bit off a piece. He knew I wanted him to, and he was trying. But no: he spat it back out on the plate.

I wanted to bargain with him—no food, no Games Workshop—but I worried that I wasn't being fair. It wasn't as if he were being deliberately uncooperative. He would sit and stare at the damned pasta all night. No food and no fun. Not for the first time, I wished someone could give me the answers.

'Can we go now?' he said.

I nodded, and Riche made straight for the door. We walked up to the Queen Street mall, where shoppers mingled with packs of high school students gathered on street corners. Riche dodged a group armed with Cokes and burgers outside Hungry Jack's. He darted from one side of the mall to the other to avoid juice stands and girls sipping soft drinks as they giggled into their phones. If mobile burgers approached, he swerved wide and shot visual daggers at the offending carrier. I followed, flushed and sweating, trying to ignore the stares his strange behaviour attracted.

Riche spotted the Games Workshop logo next to an escalator that opened directly onto the mall. We took the escalator up to the floor above and found the door off to the right. A sign on the storefront read, *No Food or Drink*. An anorexic haven. With no idea how significant this tiny war-zone would become to us in the ensuing months, I followed Riche into the dim interior.

Shelves of glossy, dark-covered rulebooks and magazines lined the side walls and stood a metre or so in front of the back wall, blocking direct sunlight from windows that overlooked the mall. The staff, all young men, wore black stovepipe trousers and red polo shirts with the Games Workshop insignia. Badges identified a Sean, two Waynes, a Trent and a Seth. One staff member sported multiple face piercings—ears, nose and eyebrows. He seemed to go by the name of Flo, although according to his badge he was one of the Waynes. These men would become my heroes.

The centrepiece of the store was the games table, roughly two by three metres—a magnificent battlefield where enemies were defeated and honour upheld. The staff had built an elaborate fortress-like structure from cardboard, netting and a pliable foam substance called green stuff. The whole thing had been painted. It was a work of art. On it, a battle was raging between two model armies of plastic and metal creatures, each two- to three-centimetre-high warrior deployed in meticulously painted battle gear. Over time, I would come to learn the names of some of these creatures: orcs, goblins, lizardmen, high elves, daemons and—the ones for which I had a particular fondness—warriors of chaos.

The staff member named Sean presided over the table. Tanned and crew cut, he would have looked as comfortable barking orders at a platoon as at this pubescent regiment. The heavy beat of the music in the background sounded like a drum call to battle. When Sean gave the word, a dice was rolled. The number determined the distance an army could advance, the distance measured with a metal ruler. Partisan onlookers urged the combatants on, shouting and booing, as if baying for blood, and it wasn't difficult to imagine mediaeval knights and chainmail and horses and swords. The air was steeped in testosterone and hummed with masculine energy and primitive urges. It couldn't have been more different from Footprints of Angels. I understood again how lonely and isolated this illness had made, and would continue to make, my son.

Nearby, several young boys were painting models at a smaller table, knaves in training for the privilege of battle. Behind them stood shelves of paint pots with wondrous names: leviathan purple, fortress grey, skull white, scab red, bubonic brown, dark angel green and, of course, chaos black.

Between the smell of glue and paint and the head-banging music and shouting, I knew I was counting on a headache if I stayed. Riche wanted to watch the game, so I retreated to a bench in an alcove adjacent to the store and watched a steady stream of teenage boys and a smattering of girls, mostly in Goth-black and studs, enter the store. When the shouting turned into cheering, I checked in on Riche. Someone's army—angels or daemons?—had trounced the enemy. Riche stood a metre away from the table, away from the other engrossed boys. He was still refusing to have his hair cut so by now it grazed his shoulders and covered his face if he didn't keep brushing it back with his hand. Elsewhere he stood out because of his hair but among the gamers he didn't look so out of place. For the first time in months, a shy smile lit up his face. It was worth a skipped meal. Just this once.

Kevin came to meet me as I pulled into the carport on Saturday afternoon. 'How was it?'

A heavy silence had fallen over Riche as we got closer to home. He shot Kevin a black look and went to his bedroom.

'That good, huh?' Kevin raised his eyebrows and shut the car door.

We took a cup of tea out to the front veranda and sat in silence for a few moments, not wanting to break the temporary accord. The constant dull roar of waves carried uphill on the hot, still air but beyond the beach break the water was smooth. I took a sip of my peppermint tea and leaned back. 'It's the best option we've got.'

I leaned my elbows on the table and rested my head in my hands while I described our interview with Jan at the clinic. Kevin listened without comment until I'd finished.

'How much does it cost?' he said, and an innocent bystander in my head observed the accord splintering. I tensed, and told him.

'Fuck!' Kevin blinked. 'That's steep.'

'For goodness sake.' My cup rattled in its saucer as I hit the table.

'Relax,' Kevin said, with the predictable contrary effect.

'Don't tell me to relax.' The innocent bystander cocked an eyebrow. Was that an adult talking or a tired, petulant child? 'Why do we always have to have this discussion about money? Don't you *want* your son to get better?'

'Of course I do,' Kevin said. 'If the clinic's the right place, then of course that's where I want him to go. But I'm allowed to comment on the cost, aren't I?'

A pause, while the justice of that seeped in.

'Sorry,' I said at last. 'I'm tired and stressed.'

Kevin gazed over my head at the distant surf. He looked back at me and gave me a tight little smile. 'It's okay. When do you start at the clinic?'

'Straight away,' I said. 'His first appointment's on Tuesday afternoon. Louise will have to go to a friend's after kindy. Andy can stay here with Dad.'

'What a nightmare.' Kevin's squinty thinking look appeared. 'What are we going to tell everyone?'

'The truth.' I sat back and folded my arms. 'It'll be easier in the long run. If we try to hide it, we'll give Riche the wrong message. He has no reason to be ashamed.'

'Are you sure?'

'Absolutely,' I said. 'I couldn't be surer.'

And this would be one of the few things I remained sure of: anorexia wasn't a crime. The brain is an organ, subject to illness like any other organ. Heart disease causes chest pain or palpitations, lung disease causes coughing and shortness of breath, gastrointestinal disease causes vomiting and diarrhoea. Brain disorders likewise produce symptoms—headaches, dizziness, behavioural changes in the case of anorexia. No reason for shame.

○

Tuesday dawned, a perfect summer day with the sun high in a cloudless sky. Riche should have been chasing his brother around the garden barefoot, with sunscreen smeared across his nose, ignoring my instructions to watch out for snakes. Instead, we were about to drive to Brisbane for his first appointment with Sonia, his new therapist. While this was not exactly the outing I would've chosen, I regarded the trip to Brisbane as a step, albeit a long one, in the right direction. I felt optimistic about my refusal to settle for the conventional local medical pathways. In a landscape of unsatisfactory options, I knew the ultra-girly environs of the clinic beat the sensory lockdown of hospital hands down.

But where was my son? He had disappeared while I was in the shower. I set off down the rainforest trail to find him, with his five-month-old silky terrier pup in tow. Trisska, Riche had named her, after the squirrel heroine in the Redwall series by Brian Jacques.

I saw Riche up ahead and Trisska spotted him too. She charged forwards and tried to jump up on him. Riche flinched, skipped backwards. He watched, with a pained expression, his dog land clumsily on the ground. She tried again. Again, Riche backed away.

'Down girl, down.' He held out his arms to stop the dog, the muscles at the corners of his mouth working as he tried to smile but failed.

'Riche?' I said. 'Is it your anorexia that won't let you touch Trisska?' An easy leap of the imagination: Trisska was a meat eater.

Riche's face screwed up and his whole body shook as he wept. Impulsively, forgetting his inability to cope with touch, I reached for my son. I remembered in time but before I could pull back, Riche fell into my arms and sobbed as if he would never stop.

I held my weeping son, a tight band constricting my chest, and stared with unseeing eyes over his head. Unable to think of a single word of comfort.

○

While Riche met with Sonia, I waited in the reception area, excluded but not, Jan had said, to blame. During therapy, Sonia would be coaching Riche on how to control his negative mind. This negative mind, so the theory went, was present in everyone but for some reason had gained the upper hand in people with anorexia. It had to be tamed to permit recovery.

The waiting room was stuffy. I fanned myself with a magazine and studied a photo of a girl hanging on the wall. Rebecca: Jan had told me her story. In the photo she wore a long, satiny gown and a hopeful smile. I searched her eyes for a sign of the imposter who had eventually enticed her to her death, two years before, in a Brisbane hospital. She had died before her mother could get her to Footprints of Angels in Melbourne. Her mother had donated the use of this house, so Jan could set up Footprints in Brisbane. I thought of Rebecca's mother. How did she get out of bed each morning?

Until now, the possibility of Riche's death from this illness had been an abstraction punctuated by the occasional dramatic statement from Kevin. Rebecca's photo changed that. It put a face to the possibility, made it personal. Rebecca's mother visited the clinic regularly; I would meet her. Despite the heat, I shivered. Finally, I understood that Riche could lose more than his childhood; this illness really could claim his life.

Sonia and Riche reappeared after an hour. Riche paced silently near the door.

'It went well,' Sonia said. 'I told Riche about myself, and we talked about the negative mind.'

She said she'd see Riche again on Thursday. Riche thanked her in a small polite voice and we left.

He looked pale and tired during the two-hour drive home. I tried several times to start a conversation, but he answered my questions in monosyllables, and after a while he closed his eyes. Exhausted as he was he couldn't refrain from tapping his fingers. Every bit of exercise counted.

○

Back in Mullumbimby, faced with my usual responsibilities, I was unable to focus exclusively on Riche. He took the opportunity to step up his exercise program and cut his food intake further. I rang Sonia. She said it was because his negative mind felt threatened by the therapy and was fighting back. This sounded plausible: a psychological duel inside his head. The real Riche needed to get the upper hand over his negative version before he died of starvation. But I couldn't shake the nagging awareness that it was just a theory. If the negative mind really existed, how did it get out of control in the first place?

On Thursday, we travelled to Brisbane for another counselling session and the first appointment with the dietician. For this week only, we were squeezing the two appointments into one day. Riche was quiet for most of the trip, but when we reached the outskirts of Brisbane, he gave a small cough and I sensed him turn to me.

'Will you stay with me when I see the dietician?' he said.

I glanced over at him. His spirit, the essence of the boy, seemed to have retreated further into his already diminished frame. My son seemed to be fading before my eyes. 'Why?' I said.

'I'm scared.'

The counselling session went smoothly. Afterwards Riche refused to eat the sandwich I'd bought or drink any water. Just before it was time to see the dietician, I found Jan and told her about Riche's reluctance to have the appointment without me.

'That's normal,' she said. 'Most sufferers don't want to discuss food, and they hate being told what to eat.'

'Well, given Riche's age, can I sit in on the first few sessions until he feels comfortable?'

Jan agreed. The dietician was unhappy with the arrangement, but for once the consumer in me prevailed. Although I thought a weekly appointment with the dietician was a waste of time for an eleven-year-old boy, I was prepared to hold my fire on that one. But I couldn't imagine what could possibly be said about Riche's food that needed to remain confidential from the very person who would be preparing it. The three of us met in the pink room. The dietician had a reserved manner and an earnest face. His first question was about what Riche liked to eat. Riche looked at me.

'It's okay,' I said.

'I'm a vegetarian.' Riche's voice was barely audible. The dietician jotted down a note on a sheet attached to a clipboard and waited for Riche to continue. Riche was silent.

The dietician nodded encouragingly but looked a little uncomfortable, possibly put off by my presence. 'What sort of vegetarian foods do you eat?'

'Tofu. Apples.' Riche delivered the list slowly and hesitantly as if the words stung his tongue. 'Strawberries, kiwifruit. Toast and Promite. Plain pasta. And broccoli.'

'What about chickpeas?'

'Mum says they go straight through you,' Riche said, his voice louder and more confident. He had parental authority to add weight to his own reasons for not eating chickpeas.

The suggestion of a smile flickered across the dietician's face. 'Maybe your mum hasn't learnt how to cook them properly.'

A fair comment. If learning how to cook chickpeas better was required, I was up to the task.

'Well that's a start,' the dietician said. 'We'll work out other foods as we go. You'll have three meals a day as well as morning tea, afternoon tea and supper. Your meal plan will be ready next week.' The dietician stood. 'Now I need to weigh you. Step onto the scales backwards. I'll cover your eyes and hold your chin up so you can't see your weight.'

This, I'd already been told, was so that Riche's so-called negative mind couldn't use the information against him. Riche swung round to glare at me. I interpreted this as a request to intervene.

'Riche's not going to want you to touch him,' I said. 'He thinks it'd make him fat.'

'I won't cover your eyes then,' the dietician said to Riche. 'I'll only hold your chin up.'

Riche gave me a panicky look and stood on the scales, his body rigid. When the dietician placed a hand under his chin, he jerked his head up as if the dietician's finger were electrically charged. The dietician glanced down at the scales, let go of Riche and recorded his weight.

I attempted to glance over his shoulder.

'Best not to know,' he said. 'That way you can't give in to questions. We ask all families to bring in their scales.'

○

It was dark by the time we saw our cottage at the end of the gravel road. Riche yawned and rubbed his eyes. 'I'm too tired to eat,' he said.

I managed to get a little water into him before he went inside, straight to the bathroom, maintaining his crab walk past the contaminated zone of the diningroom table despite his tiredness. He cleaned his teeth and went to bed. Kevin was on BlackBerry duty, so I started dinner preparations. When the meal was finished I chatted briefly to my father, kissed my mother's befuddled face goodnight, fed the dogs and cleaned up. Kevin put Andy and Louise to bed and then turned in himself.

Finally, the house was silent. I made a cup of herbal tea and sat at the table with the *Sydney Morning Herald* open in front of me. I blinked and flicked through the pages, barely absorbing any meaning, and wondered whether Riche and I would really manage the round-trip to Brisbane twice a week. Especially if he wouldn't eat at Angels.

○

By the Friday morning of the first week of commuting to Brisbane the livingroom looked like we'd been burgled: stacks of videos teetered either side of the television, books and magazines cluttered the table, and clean washing towered on a wooden sideboard. The floor was the worst, covered in fine pebbles and mud tracked in by the dogs. Bugger it, I thought, and wandered out to the veranda where my mother sat in one of the wicker chairs, her awkward mass wedged in place with cushions, a hand-knitted rug tucked over her legs.

'Hello Norma.'

I didn't bother to correct her.

Louise ran from behind the house, her sturdy brown limbs a whirl of energy. 'Watch this.' She cartwheeled on the straggly remains of our front lawn. 'What do I score?'

'Definitely a ten.' I turned to go back into the house.

'Don't go,' Louise pleaded with her eyes as well as her voice. 'Tell me what I score for this one.'

I sat on the front steps and judged several more cartwheels, all of them exemplary. Louise was unsettled by the trips to Brisbane; this was not the time to be deducting points from cartwheels.

'The best yet,' I said at last. 'Go show Andy.'

'Okay.' She went off to find her brother.

Andy spent hours in the sandpit wrestling imaginary monsters. I thought, guiltily, about his home schooling, which had dwindled to a few set exercises from his maths and English books on the days I remembered.

'If that little girl comes back, you had better ring her parents,' my mother said.

Riche emerged from the rainforest trail. He skirted the front lawn with his eyes on the ground and trudged to the side door that led from the carport to the house. He would rest in his bedroom for half an hour and then head back out to the rainforest. I was worried constantly that he would collapse from dehydration on the trail but had not the faintest idea how to stop him. Food and exercise: his two areas of intransigence. He had been heartbreakingly compliant with the trips to Brisbane even though he hated them. It was as if he sensed my distress over mealtimes and wanted to make up for his inability to eat.

Kevin joined me on the step. 'What a magic day,' he said. 'Let's take the kids to the beach.'

I broke a frond off the potted palm by the steps and shredded it. I had crawled stealthily into bed late the previous night, but as soon as I pulled the sheet over my body, Kevin had opened his eyes and reached for me. He wanted me because he loved me, he said. Every muscle in my body clenched in protest, but I had gone along with him. Something in me worried that he would look elsewhere if I continued to refuse, although he had never given me reason to think so.

I tossed the shredded palm leaf onto the lawn. 'I can't keep doing this.' I tried to keep my voice low so that my mother couldn't hear. Not that she would understand. 'I'm pulled in all directions, and Riche's getting no better. If anything, he's eating less and exercising more. I'm out of ideas, short of locking him in his room. Maybe Jan's right. Maybe he needs more appointments with Sonia.'

Kevin put a sympathetic hand on my thigh. He was always more loving after sex. 'I know this is hard for you. What do you want to do?'

I looked out over the sun-bleached landscape to the hypnotic pull of the lines of clean white breakers and felt utterly cornered. If I stayed here, Riche might die. If I left, my other kids would suffer and I might lose my marriage.

'I need to move to Brisbane with Riche.' I stared at my feet. 'I can't take on any more driving, and I need to concentrate on Riche.'

'How's that going to work?' Kevin half-turned to me, his head at a questioning angle. 'Who's going to look after Andy and Louise?'

'Jacqui might look after them.' I had trouble swallowing; I could hardly believe what I'd said. 'She hasn't taken on anything permanent since we left. She loves the kids and she's great with them. She'd probably help us out. You could ask her.'

Jacqui had baby-sat our children in Sydney if Kevin and I went to the movies or I wanted a day off. She would be devastated to hear of Riche's illness and more than likely she would be prepared to help. She could care for the children and prepare simple meals for them and for my parents. Home carers had been giving my mother her morning shower for three months now. My father would only have to manage her nappies during the day.

Kevin sat up straight. He looked as if he was going to object, but after a moment, his body slumped back against the step. He must have seen this coming.

'How long do you think you'll be in Brisbane?'

'It could be years,' I said. 'I have to do this. I have no choice. He's my child.'

My mother must have understood from the tone of our voices that all was not well because she gave me her newly lopsided smile as I walked past her into the house.

'Everything okay, Norma?'

○

I rang Jan that same day and told her. She thought it was a good idea.

'One other thing,' I said. 'Riche's hardly eating. Should we take him off food and start him on protein shakes?'

I'd been thinking about this ever since Jan told me that some of the sicker girls found it easier to take their nutrition in that form rather than proper meals. Riche knew the calorie count of all the food we ate and it was never low enough. But he wouldn't know how many calories the shakes contained; he might find it easier to get them past his anorexia.

The other problem with food was its emotional loading, its intrinsic morality. Apples were good; lollies were bad. Carrots were good; chocolate and chips were bad.

Protein shakes, on the other hand, were unfamiliar. Riche would know what the ingredients were—milk, a fruit for flavouring and the protein powder—but since he wouldn't know the exact composition of the protein powder he might find the shake more difficult to categorise as fattening.

At least that was the theory. In reality, it turned out that Riche viewed all food as bad, including protein shakes. And apples. It turned out that I might as well have fought with Riche over plates of spaghetti bolognese followed by apple pie with whipped cream as over those shakes. But I didn't know this then, and my thinking was that the shakes were a backstop: they would at least keep him alive until Sonia had helped him control this renegade negative mind. I would tell him they were his medicine: that he needed protein shakes to stay out of hospital in the same way diabetics needed insulin.

'That's a good idea,' Jan said. 'We'll start him on the shakes as soon as you move up.'

'Great,' I said and I meant it. I felt relieved to have a plan. I didn't see any downsides.

○

I searched the Yellow Pages and found the Crocodile Villas in Toowong. Long-term rates, kitchen facilities for preparing Riche's shakes, close to the clinic: perfect. I rang and booked a two-bedroom apartment, and told Riche when he came back from one of his walks. He barely reacted. I suspected he was relieved to be leaving the calorie-stuffed cottage.

Andy and Louise looked at me with white, shocked faces when I told them.

'Who'll look after me?' Louise said. I wanted to sweep her up in my arms.

'Daddy on weekends,' I said. 'And Jacqui's coming to stay. Won't that be fun? She'll draw and paint with you.'

Louise's face lit up. 'And she's better at playing games than you.'

I acknowledged my play skills had probably suffered in recent months and turned to Andy.

'Come and give me a hug.' For the first time I noticed the dark circles beneath his eyes. When he buried his head against my chest I put my arms around him and held him close.

'When will you come back?'

'I'm not sure.' *Don't think. Don't look at his eyes.* 'But Riche and I will visit you on weekends. And I'll ring you every night.'

The following morning, I packed a suitcase and stashed it in the back of the car. When Riche wasn't looking I hid a couple of bottles of chardonnay under a blanket on the back seat. *Be prepared.* Riche put a few clothes and several of his favourite books into his schoolbag and climbed in the car. I went to say goodbye to my parents. Andy, Louise and Kevin came back out to the car with me. I put my arms around my two younger children and squeezed their soft, warm bodies. Minnie stood next to them, wagging her tail. The last thing I did before I got in the car was to bend down and hug my dog.

'New plan,' I said when we got to Crocodile Villas, and told Riche about the switch to protein shakes. 'You'll find them easier than food.'

'I'm not having them,' Riche said. From his look of terror, you would have thought I was suggesting a lethal cocktail. 'You want to make me fat.'

Right. My lifelong ambition: to produce fat children.

'I don't,' I said. 'I want you to get better.'

'You're trying to make me fat.' Accusing now.

'I'm trying to keep you out of hospital. This is the only way. You have to help me.'

'I don't like the dietician.' Riche pursed his lips.

'I know,' I said. 'But you need those shakes. Okay?'

'I'll try.'

I went to my room to finish unpacking and realised with a twinge that I had no photos of Andy and Louise. I had no photos of Kevin either but that didn't worry me. The poor man had well and truly fallen victim to my scorched earth policy of blame: I still regarded him as the primary cause of Riche's illness and, while I realised knowing the cause might not help with the cure, as far as I was concerned it sure as hell explained why my son was holed up in a beige cell a hundred and fifty kilometres from home. It's no coincidence that only a few letters separate anguish from anger.

I met the dietician in the pink room while Riche waited in the reception area. He handed me a six-pack of lidded plastic cups in sorbet shades of pink, yellow, green and mauve. There was a hole in the middle of each lid for the matching plastic straw. 'You add three cups of protein powder and a spoonful of honey to a litre of milk. I suggest you use soymilk instead of cow's milk. It prevents problems with dairy allergies. And you can use light soymilk. It'll be less threatening for Riche. We make up for the calories in the powder.'

'Can you write the quantities down?' I had memorised entire volumes to earn my medical degree, but with the stress of the previous months, a simple recipe was beyond me.

The dietician agreed but asked me to destroy the paper as soon as I had committed the instructions to memory. They were very clear at Footsteps that the less information Riche had, the easier he would find it to get the shakes past his anorexia. But espionage was, apparently, a risk.

I folded the paper and hid it in a zip-up compartment of my bag. 'Now what?'

'I'll go through the routine with Riche.'

While the dietician was out of the room, I fiddled with the plastic wrapping on the cups, thinking that Louise would love the colours. The dietician reappeared with Riche, who had the wary look of a stray dog wondering if it was going to be hit.

'Sit down,' the dietician said and shut the door.

'Don't want to.' Riche stood near me, trying to telescope his body so that he occupied the smallest possible space.

'I've told Mum how to make the shakes,' the dietician said.

Riche bent his head. His long fringe fell forward and hid his face.

'You can choose whatever fruit you like to add flavour. A lot of the girls like mango and peach.'

But Riche wasn't a lot of girls. 'Strawberry,' he whispered.

Smart boy. Given free rein, he'd picked the low-calorie choice, and there'd be no changing his obsessive-compulsive mind.

'You're going to have six shakes each day.'

Riche looked up and flicked his hair off his face with a jerk of his head. 'No *way*,' he said, a wild look in his eyes, a tremor in his voice. 'That'll make me bloated. I'll kill myself.'

'Okay, you can have a plate of fruit instead of one of the shakes.' The dietician looked at me. 'Drop into the day room on your way out so I can give you the powder.'

The powder came in a clear plastic container the size of a large shoe box. It might as well have burned holes in Riche's retinae, so quickly and abruptly did his gaze bounce from the sky blue lid. I unlocked the back door of the car.

'Are you sure the seat's clean?' he said.

'I wiped it this morning.' I leaned into the car.

'Don't let my things touch anything else, will you.' Riche took a sideways step, so he could see what I was doing.

With my free hand, I pushed a towel and a magazine further along the seat.

I straightened. 'That stuff's clean. I moved it to make you feel better.'

I put the container and cups on the seat and closed the door, then I opened Riche's door. Calorie-infested handles held no fear for me. Once in my seat, I waited for him to pull across the webbing of his seatbelt, classified uncontaminated by Riche because most people hold the buckle. Then I grasped the buckle and pushed it into its clasp.

Armed with my list of ingredients, the magic powder safe in the car, I drove to the Toowong Woolworths. Riche hadn't been in a food shop in weeks, afraid, no doubt, of the calorie-crowded airspace. This time, fear that I would buy the wrong milk or, worse, sugar to spike his shake must have outweighed the fear of lurking calories. Inside the supermarket, he picked his way down the minefield of the aisle to the milk section. He searched the shelves of soymilk cartons, at least five different brands with varying fat content, trying to read labels without touching the cartons.

'We've got to hurry.' Riche shuffled from one foot to the other and wrung his hands. *Was that rotisserie chicken he smelled?* 'You can't make me drink low fat soymilk. Get Sanitarium no-fat.'

I opened my mouth to argue, but after looking at his tight, closed face, I loaded my trolley, as I did each week from then on, with Sanitarium no-fat soymilk—the one in the red carton. One thing you can say for obsessive-compulsives: they're brand-faithful.

At the homewares store Riche chose the safety of the car while I went in and bought a new blender—one uncontaminated by food. Then we returned to our motel apartment, where I scrubbed my hands and the kitchen bench under Riche's supervision. I told him he couldn't watch me while I made the shakes, sage advice from the dietician.

'You'll only put soymilk, powder and strawberries in, won't you?' He paced as he spoke. 'Don't put any honey in. I won't drink it if you put honey in.'

'No honey. I promise.'

'And don't go above that mark.' He pointed to a line a couple of centimetres below the top of the cup. 'That's how much he said.'

'I won't, but you can't watch me mix the shakes.'

Riche opened his mouth as if to argue the point, but I glared at him, and he slunk off to his room. When I closed his bedroom door after him, he was effectively imprisoned, his fear of contamination preventing him from touching the door handle.

Under the spell of Riche's obsessive-compulsive fears, I washed my hands again. Then I spooned the powder into the blender jug, poured the milk in and added a handful of strawberries. I looked for a moment at the jar of honey sitting by the toaster…No. Riche would taste it and refuse to drink the shake. I couldn't jeopardise the plan over a few calories. I turned the blender on and watched as the ingredients churned together. When it was ready, I dipped my finger in and licked it. After the initial burst of strawberry, the mixture left a metallic aftertaste. I divided the mixture between the six cups, taking care to stay below the line. Then I took a deep breath, picked up a cup, and opened Riche's door.

'It's ready,' I said, my voice calm, as if this shake had no more consequence than my morning cup of coffee. 'Come on.'

'No.' Riche's voice came out in a strangled cry. He buried his head in the pillow, and I heard a few muffled sobs.

'You have no choice,' I said. 'It's the only way I can keep you out of hospital.'

Riche raised his head. 'I can't do it,' he pleaded, this son of mine who, on our last holiday before he got sick, had summoned the courage to leap from a height of two metres into a small but deep rock pool. 'Please don't make me do it.'

'Want a nasogastric tube?' The threat in my voice made me feel sick.

Riche got off the bed and walked slowly out of his room. I gave him the cup. He held it at arm's length, stared at it for a moment, shuddered and drew his hand back, ready to slam the cup against the wall.

'Don't throw it Riche. I'll just have to make more.'

'But it's going to make me fat.'

'No it's not,' I said. 'That's the anorexia talking. Look at your arm, there's nothing to it.'

With his free hand, Riche pinched his arm and lifted the slackened skin.

'See.' His eyes filled with more tears. 'I'm fat.'

'That's skin,' I said. 'It's loose because you've lost your normal subcutaneous fat. Everybody has that, it's like a layer of insulation. Now drink.' My voice was firm, but inside I trembled.

'Are you sure you didn't put anything else in? You didn't put any sugar in, did you? Or honey? There's no honey in it is there?'

93

'No,' I said. 'I promised you I wouldn't put honey in. You have to trust me. I haven't hurt you yet, have I?'

'You're trying to make me fat.'

And so it went.

Half an hour passed before he put his lips to the straw. It took another hour of sips and questions—the same ones over and over—to finish the shake.

I rinsed the cup and left it in the sink, reflecting on what an enormous amount of courage it had taken Riche to overcome his very obvious fear. He was in the bathroom now. He made several deep throat-clearing noises and spat repeatedly. I stood outside and listened in case he vomited, but he didn't. I heard the sound of running water, and then Riche appeared, shaking his hands dry.

'Can we go for a walk?'

'Sure.' Riche's therapist had agreed to two half-hour walks each day—longer and he would burn too much energy, less and he would become agitated. The Mount Coot-tha Botanical Gardens were a couple of kilometres down the road from our apartment. And a walk in the gardens would cheer us up—we both missed our rainforest. Before we left Riche went back into the toilet, even though he had just urinated, then into the bathroom. When he came out his hands looked raw.

'Shall we wait and time it so we can have your next shake in the gardens?' I said.

'No way.' Riche sounded horrified. 'I'm not having my shake there.'

Apart from two gardeners shifting sprinklers on the grassy slopes in the Australian section of the gardens, we had the place to ourselves. We wandered down to the lake and climbed up the other side, where trails wound through a thicket of trees: lilly pillies, banksias, eucalypts, brown pines with rich, textured bark and bottle-green leaves. Water trickled over stones in man-made creeks. Cool green light filtered through the canopy. Riche stopped to look at frogs hopping in the creeks and I glimpsed a shadow of the old Riche—the passionate, energetic child I had to work to keep up with. I didn't want to leave.

Back at the apartment Riche went to the toilet three times in the next hour, shaking his hands dry each time. I understood that: he must think I had contaminated the handtowel. But I didn't know what to make of the frequency. Did he have a urinary tract infection? Had the anorexia already damaged his kidneys? Was it yet another obsession developing?

After the third visit to the toilet he said, 'If I have my shake now, can we go to Games Workshop?'

'It's a bit early.' The dietician had told me to space the shakes evenly to ensure steady nutrition through the day. On the other hand, he was volunteering. 'Okay.'

Despite the incentive of Games Workshop, the next shake took as long as the first. We worked our way several times through the same list of questions before Riche took his first sip. Between sips, he tipped the cup so that the thick liquid coated the inside surface.

'Stop that.' I could feel my heart racing. 'I know what you're doing. Now you have to wait for it to drain to the bottom of the cup.'

Riche held the cup upright for a few seconds and then turned it upside down and shook it, dripping liquid onto the carpet. I grabbed his arm and righted the cup.

'*Drink*. Or we don't go.' I hoped our neighbours had the television up loud.

When he had swallowed the last of the shake, Riche rushed to the bathroom where he spat and gargled for ten minutes. I picked up the car keys. Waited while he went to the toilet again. Finally we set off.

As soon as Riche looked comfortable at Games Workshop, I went back down the escalator, across the mall and through the shopping arcade to Borders. To beat this illness I needed to do more than supervise five protein shakes and a fruit plate each day. To beat the enemy I had to know it, which meant reading books. Borders had a good collection of books on eating disorders, unlike the suburban bookstores with their shelf-loads of diet books. I bought *Reviving Ophelia* by Mary Pipher, and *Anorexia Nervosa: A Guide to Recovery* by Lindsey Hall and Monika Ostroff. On my way back to Games Workshop, I called in at the toy department and bought a new Monopoly set to help distract Riche from his tormenting thoughts.

When I brought out the game Riche eyed it suspiciously. 'Did you take it near food?' he said.

'No,' I said. 'I bought it from Myers. They don't sell food.'

Actually they did, but Riche would never know. He was unlikely to venture beyond the cosmetics and tie departments that lined our path from the carpark elevator door to the street. After an hour or so of the game, we were both yawning, so Riche went to bed. As soon as he was asleep, I ran down to reception and bought a frozen meal to microwave. On the way back to our apartment, I detoured to collect a bottle of wine from the car. I might have forgotten photos of my family, but I had managed to nail down a good supply of chardonnay.

o

As the week dragged by, I established a routine—one thing that's not difficult with an obsessive-compulsive child.

Each day Riche had five protein shakes and at night a small plate of fruit of his choice—a never-varying selection of an apple, a kiwifruit and a handful of strawberries. He visited the clinic, walked with me in the botanic gardens and spent some time at Games Workshop. In the evenings we played Monopoly. Until the third day, that is, when I stupidly sat down next to the Monopoly board with a glass of wine. After that, the game was banished. Several times I suggested Riche have a protein shake somewhere other than the motel: at the clinic, in the park, somewhere near Games Workshop. Each time he refused. I was unwilling to upset our tenuous progress, so I didn't persist.

The routine was both mind-numbingly boring and excruciatingly tense, and consumed us. During the day I succeeded in my efforts to squash any thoughts of Andy and Louise. At night when Riche was in bed I thought of them at home with Jacqui, and my head ached with longing.

I decided we'd go home to visit them that Saturday, at the end of our first week. I'd pack a cooler with two shakes and spend a few precious hours with Andy and Louise. Catch up on their week, comb Louise's hair, ask Andy to show me what he'd done for home schooling. Feel the healthy weight of their bodies in my arms and try to squeeze in a week's worth of mothering. This would be Riche's first shake at home but surely he'd manage; he'd been eating and drinking there—a little at least—up until six days ago.

○

Minnie heard my car on the gravel track and rushed out to greet us. Her barking alerted Kevin to our arrival. He came out, smiling, and opened the passenger door. 'Hi, Riche,' he said. 'Minnie's missed you.'

Riche exited in an extraordinary levitating manoeuvre—a twisted version of look-Mum-no-hands bike riding—walked right past Kevin and turned to me.

'My shake is due in half an hour,' he reminded me and slunk off behind the cottage. It was the first time he'd refused to acknowledge his father.

'Shall I go after him?' Kevin said.

I hesitated and shook my head. 'Leave him. You'll say the wrong thing and make it worse.'

It was clear to me that Kevin had no idea how to handle his son. I didn't think there was much he could do to redeem himself in Riche's eyes, and I still wasn't too happy with him either. What I didn't see was the speed with which ignoring Kevin would become another of Riche's obsessions.

Louise and Andy came running, stories of the past week tumbling out of them as they jostled for my attention. Inside, I saw that the cottage again showed signs of my absence with newspapers and clothing piled on the table. My mother, stranded on her recliner chair, claimed me for a few minutes until I heard Riche calling me from the front lawn.

'Is it time for my shake?' he said. 'I'm not having it if it's late.'

'It's not late.'

'Is it safe to go into the bathroom to wash my hands?' He wrung his hands. His face had a pinched look.

'It's safe,' I said. 'Nothing's going to hurt you.'

Riche edged his way through the front door towards the bathroom to wash his hands. He came out to the car, and watched me take a shake from the cooler. I managed to talk him through two-thirds of it. The rest he spat on the ground.

'Please let me have the next one in Brisbane,' he said. 'It's too hard here.'

My heart sank. We'd have to leave in the next half hour in order to be there in time. Two hours to get here, two hours back, all for a one hour visit. But I couldn't afford to have Riche lose more weight. We had no safety margin.

I found Andy in the sandpit, his favourite place to dream and relax. He cut a forlorn figure in track pants and a hand-me-down T-shirt from Riche.

'I haven't spent much time with you.' His shoulders sagged.

'I'm sorry.' I hugged him and left him in his pit.

'Do you have to go?' Louise said.

'Yes, I do.' Can a beating heart burst like a pipe under pressure? 'We'll talk on the phone.'

Kevin lifted Louise from my arms. He leant forward to kiss me.

'This is your fault.' I lashed out from the depths of my hurt. 'Look what you've done to your son.'

I fastened Riche's seatbelt without touching him, pressed my foot hard to the accelerator. The tears spilled from my eyes as my family disappeared in the swirling dust in the rear-vision mirror.

'Don't park near a bad shop,' Riche said from the front passenger seat. He sat with his feet carefully placed in front of him and his elbows jammed to his sides, away from the door and the gearbox.

I drove at a crawl, keeping an eye out for the Walton Bridge Medical Centre, while I tried to scan the hazards of the shopping centre carpark through Riche's eyes. The liquor store and the bakery were obvious. The calorie traps in the chemist were more subtle—peppermints and cough drops on the counter, not to mention all those enriching, and therefore fattening, face and hand creams. Not a toy store or menswear in sight.

Finally I spotted the medical centre. It fronted right onto the carpark so I would be spared the ordeal of exposing Riche to the perils of the recycled air in the arcades. And miraculously there was a vacant parking spot right outside. As I pulled in I noticed the blue wheelchair symbol painted on the bitumen, shrugged and shut off the engine. If a parking inspector came by I'd pay the fine but I had no ethical qualms. Riche's condition disabled him pretty effectively, I felt.

'Come on, your appointment's in five minutes.' I unbuckled Riche's seatbelt and opened my door.

'What if she's like the last doctor?'

'She won't be,' I said, with more confidence than I felt. I knew little about this doctor. Still, Riche's therapist said we needed to have medical supervision, so here we were. At least this doctor was already seeing another patient from Footprints of Angels and was familiar with their non-traditional methods. Fingers crossed.

Inside, our appointment time came and went and at last a voice called for Riche. A slim middle-aged woman dressed neatly in a plain skirt with a button-up blouse stood in the doorway, folder in hand.

Dr C ushered us into a small consulting room, sat behind the desk and offered me a seat in front.

'Would you like to sit down, Riche?' she said.

The question triggered a furious look tinged with his familiar plea for intervention.

'He can't,' I said. 'He's afraid of contamination.'

'Oh.' The doctor maintained an unruffled expression. 'Well, how can I help you?'

I summarised Riche's medical history for her. 'He's doing well at Footprints,' I said. 'His therapist just wants to make sure he's medically safe to remain an outpatient.' I took a quick breath and went on with my sales pitch before the doctor could interrupt. 'I'm sure he'll be fine. He's managed five protein shakes and a plate of fruit each day for a whole week now.' I didn't mention that half the fruit went uneaten.

The doctor scratched away at her notepad. I took the opportunity to search for clues to her personality. A piece of paper stuck out from under the corner of her leather desk mat. The word 'Jesus' leapt out of the upside-down print. I wanted to take this as a good sign—*suffer the little children to come unto me*. The Christianity of my youth had rained brimstone, but still. Other than that one word, the doctor's desk was covered with the usual clutter of pens and pharmaceutical company notepads. Dr C finished her notes.

'I'd better have a look at you, Riche,' she said.

Riche reared back and gave me yet another loaded look, more

furious than the last, as if to say I had betrayed him by bringing him here and exposing him to whole new legions of undercover calories.

'Can you wash your hands?' I said. 'So Riche knows they're clean.'

The doctor looked uncertain. 'All right.' A carbolic smell filled the room as she pressed on the soap dispenser. She held her hands out for Riche to inspect. 'Is that better?'

Riche nodded and grunted but stayed right where he was.

'The couch,' I said.

My son looked at the door but must have decided that the handle was riskier than the crisp white sheet: he took a couple of tentative steps and balanced on the edge of the couch.

'Can you manage with him like that?' I said. Riche looked even more agitated than when we'd seen the doctor nearer home. I was worried that he might try to lash out—it would be a defensive action in his mind. I positioned myself, ready to block him if necessary.

'I'll see how we go.'

Dr C reached for Riche's arm; he pulled it away.

'The doctor has to take your pulse,' I said.

Riche moved his arm an inch towards the doctor, who held his wrist as carefully as if it were broken while she looked at her watch.

'What are you getting?' I asked.

'It's slow—forty-eight,' Dr C said. She turned back to Riche. 'I need to measure your blood pressure.'

She picked up the pressure cuff and the stethoscope that dangled from the stand. Riche whimpered. He held his arms close to his body, fists tightly clenched, and leaned away.

'Hold out your arm.' I hated seeing him so afraid but it had to be done. 'It won't hurt.'

An even more furious look, but he held out his arm. Dr C fastened the cuff around his upper arm, and pumped it up. She placed the stethoscope's diaphragm over the pulse point in the soft crease of his elbow.

'The systolic is low,' she said. 'Eighty.' She pumped in more air and then listened as she let the cuff slowly deflate. A few seconds later, she removed the cuff and unhooked the stethoscope from her ears. 'I can't get the diastolic, but we'll leave it at that.'

She returned to her desk. Riche shimmied forward, keeping his hands well clear of the sheet, and climbed down from the couch. The doctor smiled at him. 'Why don't you wait in the reception area while Mum and I talk.'

Thank God. No dressing down in front of my child this time. I didn't need to be asked to open the door.

'You won't be long, will you?' Riche said to me. 'What's the time? Is it nearly time for my next shake?'

Gritted teeth. 'I'll be out soon. We'll go straight to the motel.'

Dr C waited for me to close the door and sit down. 'Richard might be better off in hospital,' she said, her voice serious but gentle. 'He's very sick. He probably needs nasogastric feeds.'

'No,' I said. I leaned forward and pleaded my case: he would never cope with hospital. He would panic whenever food appeared or anyone tried to touch him. You've seen how frightened he is. Busy nursing staff on a general paediatric ward wouldn't understand. They'd just think he was deliberately uncooperative and he'd be labelled naughty.

The doctor countered with her clinical findings: he's showing signs of dehydration. Pulse and blood pressure low. He's at risk of collapse, death even. *You know that.*

I did. I was well aware that cardiac complications were one of the most common causes of death in the acute stage of anorexia. But there were risks on both sides. And my gambling instincts told me I had time. The shakes routine was excruciating but we were managing. I'd figure out a way of getting more water into him soon.

The doctor looked at me. Perhaps she was expecting me to give in. But I'd learned a thing or two from my son about begging, and started back in: I was only asking for a week to stabilise him myself. We were already on the right track. It would be easier for him. Ultimately, it might decrease the duration of his illness. You know how the cycle goes—yo-yoing weight, in and out of hospital for years. I didn't want to sign Riche up for that. And wasn't it possible that active swallowing itself was beneficial? Mightn't it do more to combat the obsessive cycle than passive nasogastric feeding?

It was just an intuition but it sounded reasonable to me.

The doctor wrinkled her forehead, then leaned forward and planted her elbows on the desk. She let her gaze fall to her hands, her fingers laced together. *Here's the church and here's the steeple, open the door and please tell this doctor to let me take Riche home.* She unlaced her fingers and looked at me.

'We'll have to get some blood tests done before I decide,' she said. 'If there are problems with his electrolytes, or any signs of organ damage,' and here I thought of Riche's frequent visits to the toilet, 'he'll need to be admitted.' Her voice had an air of finality.

I sat back in my chair. 'Thank you.'

'Mind you, I'll have to see him several times a week until he's stable.'

That was fine by me. A warning from the dietician at Footprints of Angels still reverberated in my ears, 'We must watch out for the refeeding syndrome for the first few weeks.' Apparently the body's metabolism adapted to starvation. Sudden large quantities of food inundated the system like floodwaters, with equally devastating results—multi-system organ damage and potentially dangerous electrolyte imbalances that could cause cardiac arrhythmias and death. The worse the starvation, the greater the risk of serious problems.

Monitoring his condition several times a week made perfect sense. If it were possible to have him admitted for an initial week or two, I would have happily agreed, but that didn't seem to be an option. Much as I dreaded a long-term hospital admission, however, I knew that if Riche's condition deteriorated I would call an ambulance. Promise or no promise.

Dr C filled in a request form. 'Get these done today,' she said.

'I've marked them urgent, so ring me tonight, and we'll discuss the next step.'

'Thank you.' I started to rise.

'Oh, and…' She paused while I sat down again. 'I want you to take Richard to a psychiatrist.'

I frowned: this was not good news. It meant one more doctor to plead with. I nodded slowly and sucked in a deep breath. 'Okay,' I said. 'If you think that's really necessary.'

'I do,' Dr C said. 'The one I have in mind has a good reputation. If he's not happy, Riche will have to go to hospital. I'll make an appointment right now.'

This doctor was not going to let me get away with anything. But I respected her approach and appreciated her concern for Riche. She opened an address book, ran a finger down a page and dialled a number. I listened as she relayed Riche's history. Then she fell silent for a moment before continuing.

'Yes, she seems reliable.' She smiled at me. 'She has a medical degree.' More silence. 'Okay, I'll tell her that.' She hung up the telephone.

'He's unhappy with Riche not being in hospital,' she said, 'and wants to see him urgently next Tuesday, 5 pm.' She passed on the psychiatrist's advice that I should take Riche straight to an emergency department if I was worried before then.

I would be doing lots of worrying before then, but I wouldn't be going near any emergency departments if I could help it.

○

In the car, I strapped Riche in and checked the request slip for the blood tests and the referral to the psychiatrist. Unlike the doctor nearer to our Mullumbimby home, Dr C was not an envelope sealer. In fact Dr C was proving a godsend. The referral was straightforward, as were the blood tests. Dr C had requested a full blood picture, urea and electrolytes, liver function tests, calcium and blood sugar levels, and thyroid function tests. All information that would be useful and that I wished the previous doctor had ordered. It would have either spurred me into action or saved me some anguish.

The tests would show if starvation had damaged Riche's internal organs, they would show any electrolyte disturbances, and indicate the severity of his dehydration. Blood never lies. I put the forms in my bag and drove out onto Waterworks Road. Aptly named, I thought. Water works very well in the treatment of dehydration. If only I could convince Riche.

○

My son had said very little since we left the doctor's surgery. Now he looked at me with frightened eyes. 'What did she say?' Translated roughly, this meant, 'Is she going to put me in hospital?'

'She's ordered some blood tests,' I said. 'And she's sending us to a psychiatrist. A good one, so don't worry.' I kept quiet on the subject of hospital.

After the next hand-washing and protein-shake session, I looked up the nearest pathology laboratory and marshalled my son. He grumbled but manoeuvred himself into the car without much fuss. It's possible he saw blood-letting as a potential aid to weight loss.

'Will it hurt?' he said, as we drove through tree-lined suburban streets past Queenslander houses sitting high on stilts, a picture of orderliness with their neatly painted lattice, their gardens of box and gardenias.

'It feels like a pin prick,' I said. *If you get a decent technician.*

We didn't. After the frowns and the explanations and the hand-washing and the threats and the reassurances, the woman put a tourniquet around Riche's arm.

'Make a fist.' He did. 'Now open and close it a few times.'

Riche's knuckles whitened as he obeyed. All eyes were on the inside of his elbow—the cubital fossa—where a thin blue line formed as a vein filled beneath his skin. The woman tore open a small sachet. You could almost smell Riche's fear above the alcohol-soaked swab. The woman wiped his skin, took a butterfly needle from a silver tray and inserted it into Riche's arm. She pushed it towards the thread-like vein which collapsed, as if in protest, at the touch of the sharp point. The woman wiggled the needle around and pushed it further in. Still no blood. She took the needle out and reinserted it. Riche winced and bit his lip. I grimaced in sympathy. With no body fat to cushion the pain, it must have hurt like hell. The woman removed the needle again. She was sweating profusely.

'I'm sorry,' she said. 'It's not usually this hard. His veins are terrible.'

They were. I didn't envy her. She re-swabbed the area and had another stab at the task. I hoped I'd never put any of my patients through an ordeal like this. Riche screwed up his face. Silent tears rolled down his cheeks. This time the woman found a vein. She taped the plastic butterfly wings to Riche's arm and reached for the specimen tubes, but it took forever to coax enough blood from his shivering body to fill them.

Afterwards, Riche huddled in the front seat of the car, looking completely wrung out. 'Please don't take me back there,' he said. 'It hurt.'

We drove back to the motel and the four-thirty shake—another torturous hour of questions and cup-tipping and sipping, followed by tooth-cleaning and spitting.

Then I took Riche to the Roma Street Parklands, where paths wound between beds of flowering agapanthus and petunias and marigolds in glorious cascading colours, past a waterfall and across a bridge, and the air was filled with the sound of rushing water. Each time we passed someone Riche stared suspiciously, but no one was carrying food and we made it back to the car without incident.

I rang Dr C shortly afterwards.

'Did you get the results?' Papers rustled at the other end of the line.

'Yes. They confirm that Riche's moderately dehydrated,' the doctor said. 'His urea is elevated—8.8. But there are no signs of organ damage.'

'That's good.' I felt my muscles slacken with relief: the frequent toilet visits were probably just another manifestation of Riche's burgeoning obsessions.

'Yes. But if he isn't better hydrated soon,' her voice grew louder, perhaps to emphasise her resolve, 'I'll have to send him to hospital for an IV drip. We'll repeat the tests on Thursday.'

I was pitting myself against the system. If I allowed the doctor to admit Riche for an intravenous drip, I would find myself kicked out of the driving seat. The admitting doctor would notify the psychiatrist on call, who would likely take one look at my son's starved body and deluded psyche and refuse to discharge him. A routinely inedible hospital meal would appear with a nasogastric tube hot on its heels. And just like that, Riche would have secured his spot on the merry-go-round. When it came to learning the anorexic tricks of the trade—sabotaging the tube, diluting the fluid with water—my clever son would be the master apprentice. Why, he could even sign up for a crash course in vomiting and laxative abuse if he wanted.

My mission was clear. I strode into Riche's room armed with a glass of icy cold water.

'I'm not thirsty,' Riche said when I offered it to him. He licked his dry and cracked lips, and sank, trembling, back on his pillows. From the look he gave me you would have thought I was Eve with the apple.

'You'll die if you don't drink more.'

'You can't make me.' His tone was more fearful than belligerent.

I stood there, my useless glass of water in hand, while Riche's kidneys excreted yet more urea into his already concentrated urine. *You can bring an anorexic to water, but you can't...* There had to be a way.

'You have to help me keep my promise.'

My last resort and it sounded lame even to me. Moreover, I was beginning to realise that while my promise to keep Riche out of hospital bought me his trust, it came at a price. I had lost the leverage of the threat of hospital, although by asking for his help to keep my promise, I was, in essence, threatening to break it. And Riche knew this.

'I'll die if you put me in hospital.' He closed his eyes as if he could remove the threat by making me disappear.

Jan had said that Riche should give up home schooling because he would need all his energy to fight this illness. She was right about giving it up—no way could Riche concentrate. But as I looked at my son, so fragile and vulnerable, I knew that if I were to depend on his energy, we were finished. The strength had to come from me.

Time to strategise. I wandered out to the living room and settled down to read more of Mary Pipher's *Reviving Ophelia*. Maybe I would find the answers here. As I read, I made notes.

Pipher viewed anorexia as a metaphor for life: a complicated life is reduced to a single issue—weight. Was this a prelude to parent-blaming, I wondered? Many children live complicated lives. Not all of them develop anorexia. But she seemed less censorious than Hilde Bruch, whose book *The Golden Cage* I'd tossed aside when I reached the sentence, 'The question is what goes on in these seemingly well-functioning families so that the girls grow up deficient in self-esteem, unable to meet and enjoy the new opportunities of adolescence and adulthood.'

A few pages later, Pipher made a claim that particularly caught my eye: people with anorexia must see the illness as their enemy, she wrote, and make a conscious decision to fight if they are to recover. Okay, Ms Pipher, your theory seems to be in line with Jan's comment. Maybe you're both right. But as it stands it is an abstraction. It will hold no sway with a sick eleven-year-old boy. You—or rather I— will have to give my boy concrete reasons to fight.

As I pondered this, I found it surprisingly difficult to do. The best

I could come up with was that Riche's illness wouldn't let him touch his dog Trisska, and kept him in Brisbane, away from home. The concept troubled me for other reasons, just as I had been troubled when the receptionist at Footprints of Angels told me they didn't take clients who were in denial. There had to be a way to help all patients. Even those in denial, even those who showed no desire to fight. Those like my son.

The last thing I read before bed was a brochure that had arrived that day from the Queensland Eating Disorders Association. It suggested that over-protective mothers of anorexic children should get a hobby.

I shredded it, with vindictive pleasure, into small pieces. I had a hobby, a fulltime hobby: the game of survival. It was a game I was determined to win, one round at a time.

The first round was water.

Riche baulked at his scheduled Thursday blood test on the grounds that it would hurt. My assurances that we were going to a different technician, one who was trained to take blood from children, made no difference. Time to test the new strategy. *Are you listening, Mary Pipher?*

'Your anorexia—it won't let you touch Trisska, right?' I said, as if the illness were some balaclava-wearing hoodlum from the tough side of town. 'If you want her back you have to fight.'

The words had the effect of a sharp backhander to the chin and Riche slumped on his bed. He resisted for a moment, then allowed me to hold him in my arms before we went to the car. A hollow victory.

As we headed north down Jephson Street, a willy-willy picked up scraps of paper and leaf litter from the gutter. I didn't believe the Aboriginal stories of my childhood. It was air currents and pressures that caused these skittering winds, not evil spirits. But still I shivered and turned up the heat. It would at least blast Riche's veins into a slightly more dilated and accessible state.

As I swung the car into Milton Road a loud thud from Riche's side of the car caught me by surprise. I eased back on the accelerator and took my eyes off the road in time to see Riche bang his head on the window—another thud—and rake his face with his hands. A fresh scratch ran the length of his cheek.

'Stop it!' I'm guessing I shouted. Horns honked and wheels squealed as impatient drivers in the cars behind changed lanes and overtook us.

'If you're going to hurt me I might as well hurt myself,' Riche said in a hollowed out voice as he continued to bang his head.

I checked the rearview mirror: an unrelenting stream of cars followed us. Heart pounding, I tightened my grip on the steering wheel and glanced across at Riche's door to check the lock. If his fear of the blood test overrode his fear of the door handle he might jump out into the traffic. But the door was locked. The drumbeat of his head against the window was unbearable. Unable to stop him, I focused on the endless white line that stretched out in front of me and drove on to the pathology lab.

There the specially qualified technician sweated and muttered under her breath while I clenched my fists and closed my eyes, and Riche cried out in agony as the needle hit a nerve instead of a vein.

○

Phone conversation with Dr C:

Dr C: Riche's urea levels have risen to 9.9.
Me: A few more days. *Please!*
Dr C: We'll see what the psychiatrist says on Tuesday.

That evening, Riche talked more than he had in weeks.

'I'm lonely.' He sat on his bed and wrapped his arms around his bent legs. His voice shook. 'I have no friends. I'm too scared to talk to people in case I say something wrong.'

Riche had never had trouble making friends, quite the contrary. The illness was eating away at his confidence, and this new hesitancy tore at my heart.

'It takes time,' I said, knowing how inadequate my words were. 'The girls at Footprints of Angels seem nice.'

'But there are no boys. I miss Trisska.'

'Well maybe we should go down to Mullumbimby for the weekend?'

Riche shook his head, his eyes fierce. 'Dad doesn't understand, and Trisska looks so happy to see me but then…I can't even pat her.' Tears streamed down his face. 'I hate anorexia. I want to get better.'

I wondered about his words. For the first time he'd been able to talk about the illness as something separate from him. More than that, something he wished gone. But I knew better than to be too excited. Unlike a messy room, anorexia was not a lifestyle choice. It seemed to me that Riche could no more choose to recover than someone with cancer.

○

Unexpected phone conversation with Dr C at 9 am on Saturday morning:

> *Dr C*: The psychiatrist is uncomfortable. He's ordered an interim ECG to check on Riche's heart. Can you come in?
> *Me*: Of course.

The ECG—barely tolerated by Riche—was normal. Dr C ordered further blood tests, 'To be on the safe side.' This time I took him to the laboratory at the Wesley Hospital. It had taken three hours after his protein shake to persuade him to get back in the car for another round of needles.

A woman appeared in the waiting room. 'Richard?' She smiled. Her accent was Irish. 'I'm Trish. Will you come with me?'

Riche followed her without a murmur. I waited for the yelling, but it never came. Riche appeared a few minutes later with Trish behind him.

'The results should be ready soon,' she said. 'It was nice to meet you, Riche.'

Phone conversation with Dr C:

Dr C (sounds worried): Riche's urea has risen to 12.3.

Me: His ECG was normal. A few more days. *Please!*

Dr C: This is your last chance. The psychiatrist's word will be final.

The running tally on health professionals, including the Footprints therapists, was eight. This psychiatrist would be number nine. Riche stood near the car, all tense angles and contorted face—a fragile piece of installation art in the concrete carpark. 'I don't want to see the psychiatrist.'

No surprises there. I trotted out my either-or spiel. Here or hospital; take your pick. (Although, technically speaking, 'here' *was* a hospital, even if we were just visiting the outpatient wing.)

'You're not tricking me, are you?' Riche said. 'You're not going to leave me here?'

'Of course not. I promise.' A stone weight settled somewhere in the middle of my chest. The results from that morning's blood test showed that his urea had decreased a fraction to 11.4. Would that satisfy the psychiatrist?

'I'll die if you put me in hospital.' Potentially true, if melodramatic. Rebecca, the girl in the photo at Footprints of Angels, had died in hospital. Hospitalisation was no guarantee of recovery. So no: I wouldn't hospitalise my son unless absolutely necessary. For now, my promise was currency for his trust in me.

Inside the hospital entrance, we found a staircase that took us up to empty corridors between white painted walls. A muffled shriek cut through the stillness.

Riche jumped. 'What was that?'

'A patient,' I said. 'No one's going to hurt you.'

I stopped a nurse to ask for directions. As she spoke, Riche swung round as if to flee, then stopped short. A woman in a checked dress and a white cotton cap was pushing a dinner trolley like a battering ram of calories up the corridor behind us. The generic smell of institutional steamed vegetables drifted towards us. Riche shuddered.

I thanked the nurse. 'This way, Riche.' He had no alternative but to follow me to the doctor's consulting rooms.

I didn't waste my breath offering Riche a seat. With those dinner trolleys patrolling the corridors, no seat was safe. He prowled up and down like an emaciated lion.

A young woman in a floor-length dressing gown shuffled past him, her eyes fixed on the floor ahead. She moaned loudly as she walked, oblivious to our presence. And there we were, the three of us, each in our own version of reality; mine, in some ways, as alternative as theirs. Riche drew close to the wall, brooding eyes fixed on the girl's receding back until she disappeared into a room and pulled the door shut. He shifted his gaze to me.

'Get me out of here. Please!' he said. 'This place scares me.'

'She's sick,' I said. 'She can't help it.' The girl's behaviour was no more unusual than Riche's.

I wanted to take his hand and make a dash for the door but I forced myself to stay in my plastic seat. I had no choice. More than just a feeling of no choice, it represented a full-scale backslide to my archaeological dig, due, perhaps, to a combination of my recent reading and the familiar hospital smells—floor polish and disinfectant—that tugged at my memory with an almost gravitational strength. I was the student here and the psychiatrist the expert or, as Dr C had said, the final word. I found myself wanting to believe that, as the most highly qualified person we'd seen to date, he would uncover the cause—the mysterious cause—that the other health professionals and I had missed, and that it would prove to be the key to Riche's recovery.

I began my familiar life review. I wanted to have my story straight.

In the past I had considered myself a competent parent: seven out of ten; maybe eight on a good day. I was an unimaginative cook but fed my children a balanced diet. Occasional treats: no one was going to lump me with the title of food police. Apart from that recent slip-up with my father. And one incident, a wits-end situation, when Andy gagged over the spaghetti I'd forced him to eat. I raised my voice every so often—wet towels and squabbles mainly—but remained cheerful most days. I read bedtime stories, had a working knowledge of the drawbridge in the Brio train set and could carry the tune from *Thomas the Tank Engine*. When Riche was four years old, I watched *The Love Bug* on at least thirty consecutive days.

So I had got some things wrong. Who hadn't? During my misspent years as a corporate wife I'd fussed over smudges on the black marble kitchen benches. I was late with vaccination appointments. I confused the local Toys-R-Us with a playground. And Louise's devotion to Pluggy, a bright yellow dummy embellished with a stegosaurus, guaranteed a future relationship with the orthodontist.

It got worse, though. Mother tries to cook dinner for three young children while father travels overseas, eldest child refuses to comply with some long-forgotten request. Mother loses temper and lands a smack on child's bottom. It happens a handful of times, there are tears, the child tells his mother he thinks she doesn't love him. Devastated, she apologises. More tears. It never happens again. But were there long-term consequences?

Perhaps I'd been easy on myself in the past when it came to parenting. Perhaps the score was more like three or four. Because now, compiling all my mistakes, it seemed clear to me that Kevin and I were the bad guys. The only question was which of us was worse: Kevin with his bluff failure to understand his sensitive son, or me with my endless mistakes. Well, the psychiatrist would set us straight on that count. Then we'd fix the damage. Hell, we'd sign up for a parentectomy if that would persuade Riche to eat.

The psychiatrist appeared, neatly suited under a white coat. During my family medicine training in medical school, our tutors had discouraged us from wearing white coats except during messy procedures. They built a barrier, they said, between patient and doctor.

The psychiatrist smiled. 'I'll talk to you first,' he said to me. This seemed promising. I gave Riche a reassuring smile and left him to his pacing. The psychiatrist ushered me in and closed the door. 'Take a seat.'

The psychiatrist introduced himself, then picked up his pen and took a blank sheet of paper from the file on his desk. 'Tell me about Riche.'

'It's a long story,' I said. 'It starts with my mother.' Or at least her illness. That was item one on my list of possible causes.

I spoke about my mother's aneurysm and subsequent medical mishaps; perhaps, I suggested, it was part of the general trauma out of which Riche's illness arose. The psychiatrist said nothing to persuade me otherwise. He took a few notes while I talked, but for the most part his eyes were on me. In spite of the white coat, I warmed to his concerned expression.

Item two on my list was the fancy boys' school in Sydney where Riche was bullied, a situation that came to light when I found Riche crying in his room one Sunday afternoon. Previously, he had gone off happily to school each day. He signed up for every available activity: the orchestra—first the cello, which he practised naked each night, and then the trumpet, blowing with vessel-popping vigour—and the choir, more for the drama of the floor-length white robes than the singing. He represented the school in chess, debating and swimming. He won the inaugural academic scholarship for a boy entering senior primary school. All in all, he was a rather short tall poppy just waiting to be hacked off, Australian style, at the knees. And a small group of boys happily assigned themselves the task.

The bullying was subtle and ongoing, and perfectly pitched. The goal: get the victim into trouble by making him cry out during class or assembly. The technique: sit behind the victim and poke him in the ribs. Hardly a capital offence, and likely motivated more by mischief than genuine malice, but devastating to a perfectionist child, one who wanted to do well and never harmed anyone.

The psychiatrist gave me a questioning look. 'What did the school do?'

'I went to see the headmaster,' I said. 'Several times in fact.' Should I have gone in more? Demanded action? 'Nothing much happened. Riche thought the headmaster implied he was partly to blame.'

'Sounds frustrating,' the psychiatrist said.

'It was,' I said. 'But worse, Riche changed. He lost his spark. That's when we first thought of home schooling. Then 9/11 happened.' Item three on the hit list. 'It shook Riche to the core.'

The psychiatrist glanced at his notes. 'How old was Richard then?'

'Ten,' I said. 'He saw too much on television.' I looked down at my lap. He saw too much because I couldn't take my eyes off the pictures of devastation.

The psychiatrist nodded. 'Go on.'

'Kevin had scheduled a conference call with a lawyer in the World Trade Center for that morning,' I said. 'The man was a friend of ours, an American married to an Australian. We heard he was okay, but… It all felt so close to home. Kevin worked across the road from the Trade Center when we lived in New York.'

The psychiatrist made a few more notes.

Later that day, I said, a teacher had called from school to tell me Riche seemed anxious about the possibility of a third world war. The psychiatrist looked serious. 'Third world war? That's quite an intense reaction.'

'Riche took it personally,' I said. I didn't mention the predictions of American retaliation I'd made over breakfast that morning, unable to further dob myself in. 'He was born in New York. When the US started to bomb Afghanistan, Riche wanted to give up his American citizenship. He didn't believe in a violent solution. And he said he no longer felt safe.'

'He's very young to worry about these things.'

'I know.' I suspected the fault lay with me. I had encouraged my children to take an interest in the world beyond our backyard when I should have left them to make mudpies in the sandpit. This, too, I kept to myself. 'On top of all this, my mother's condition deteriorated so I flew back to Perth with the children.'

I had the psychiatrist's full attention: he might hear a lot about family dysfunction but he probably rarely heard such a well-organised narrative.

Enter item four: my mother-in-law. She had volunteered to mind the children so I could visit my mother in the intensive care unit.

Kevin's mother loved being a grandmother, just as she had loved being a mother, and always welcomed her grandchildren's visits. Problems sometimes arose due to our very different child-rearing philosophies. But there was no sign of displeasure that day when she opened her door and swept the children into her arms.

I looked at the psychiatrist. 'And everything was fine when I left. When I got back, a few hours later, Riche was looking shattered and his grandmother was evasive.'

I had taken one look at him and got him out of there. What emerged on the way home was that Riche, a champion of justice, had got into an argument with my mother-in-law over the US involvement in Afghanistan. He didn't like her attitudes. He told her it was wrong that innocent men, women and children were dying, that their deaths would never compensate for the American loss.

I discussed the argument with Riche at home, but I was sorting through fifty years of accumulated junk in my mother's cupboards and not paying full attention.

'The next day my mother-in-law rang and she seemed to want to make amends. She wanted to take Riche out.'

I told her I would ask Riche. She insisted he was a child—I should just tell him what to do—but for once I stood my ground with her and asked Riche. He didn't want to go but I said his nana's invitation was a peace offering and didn't he think he could do it for Dad and me? Then he agreed, and I made the call.

The following day, as we waited for her, Riche said I was forcing him. I looked at the psychiatrist. 'And I was.' I pressed my lips together in a moue of regret. 'He was right and I was wrong.'

'Because you expected him to make up with his grandmother?'

'Because I believed—still believe—that being a mother, being older and more experienced, confers responsibility, not control.' I paused and thought of a beloved aunt. She'd taught me that we owed our children everything, not the other way round. We'd brought them into the world: they hadn't been given the choice. 'I may have got some things wrong, but not that. It's a fundamental principle for me. I've never tried to force my children to do things they thought were wrong. Riche knew that, he's always known it. He was right to feel betrayed.'

The psychiatrist's face showed he was still in my thrall. I might be a bad mother but I had one hell of a story. 'Anyway that's what I did. I decided to ask her to talk to him. I thought they might sort out their differences. Actually I hoped she might apologise for what she said to Riche.'

'She doesn't sound like the type to apologise to a child.'

'She wasn't,' I said. 'My expectations were completely unrealistic. She's old school: elders know better. That's not her fault.' I broke off for a second and leaned against the straight back of the chair. 'Is this stuff relevant?'

'Yes.' The psychiatrist had abandoned his notes, and I had long since forgotten his white coat.

I needed him to understand the impact of the confrontation on

Riche. And to do that I had to become, once more, the mother who stood by and watched, as useless as a dress-store dummy. The time travel was easy. Some memories retain their sharp edges.

Eyes closed, I pictured myself as I waited in the shade under the veranda of my parents' house. I remembered looking at the pot plants, wilting on a white metal trolley, like a pram skeleton, and at an assortment of shrubs—grevilleas, jade, plumbago. The air smelled of bore water and dust.

It was hot, at least twenty-seven degrees, by the time Kevin's mother arrived. She asked if Riche was ready. I said he didn't want to go. I told her some of the things she'd said the day before had upset him, and suggested she talk them over with him.

Her smile cooled a few degrees, but she went inside. I followed.

I looked at the psychiatrist; his attention hadn't wandered.

'That was a mistake. I expected her to behave in an uncharacteristic way,' I said. 'But she didn't. She got mad at Riche, told him he was narrow-minded, that she was simply trying to show him another point of view. Riche nearly choked on that. She said he should have rung and cancelled, that she had plenty of friends who would have been happy to spend the day with her. Riche told her I had forced him. That was the thing, you see, he might hold strong opinions but he's an obedient child. It wouldn't have occurred to him to disobey me.'

I had noticed Andy and Louise huddled together, trying to dodge the bullets, so I hustled Riche and his grandmother outside. They squared off and, telling myself I shouldn't interfere, I stood to the side and watched the argument escalate until finally she stomped off down the driveway.

If only time travel really were a possibility. Riche's deathly pale face and goggling eyes will stay with me forever. When I asked him if he was okay, he nodded and I believed him. Or at least told myself that I believed him. Then he said, voice shaking, hurt etched in the crinkles around his eyes, 'I don't ever want to see her again.'

He was ten-and-a-half years old. Within months he would be exercising like an Olympic champion on a diet that wouldn't sustain a grasshopper.

The psychiatrist picked up his pen again. 'That must have been very traumatic for your son.'

'It was,' I said. 'I should have stepped in, ended the conversation. I didn't understand how far Riche's intellectual maturity was ahead of his emotional maturity. Or how badly hurt he was. How often do adults say and do things casually that wound children? Kevin's mother was just being herself.'

The psychiatrist nodded slowly and made a quick note. Was he sentencing Riche to hospital? I wished I could decipher his upside-down scrawl.

'So did you sort out the problem with Kevin's mother?'

I shook my head. 'No. I was busy organising my parents' move.' I'd left Perth without speaking to either her or my father-in-law.

Four items so far. One constant, apart from Riche, in each of them: me, I thought, self-blame tugging at me like quicksand.

'Riche seemed okay,' I said. 'But now...'

'What did Riche think of the move?' the psychiatrist said.

'He loved it.' I gave a small rueful laugh. 'Well, at least he said he did. The problem was Kevin.' Item five.

'Did he change his mind?'

'No,' I said. 'But the long commute tired him out. 780 kilometres. He was grumpy on weekends.'

I told the psychiatrist how betrayed Riche had felt by Kevin's repeated attempts to get him to apologise to his grandmother. 'It injured Riche's sense of justice,' I said. 'He didn't think he'd done anything wrong. He felt like he was being pushed around, just because he's a child.'

The psychiatrist nodded.

I went on, 'So this was all around the time that Riche started exercising and cutting back on food.' I described Riche's activities—

the circus training, athletics and martial arts that gradually gave way to hours of walking—and the insidious decrease in his food intake.

I moved on to my mother's condition. 'Riche's absolutely terrified he'll be hospitalised. He's said he would never want to go anywhere near a hospital after seeing what it did to his grandmother.' Item six and still counting. 'And then there were all the articles on childhood obesity in the papers. They caught Riche's attention.' I paused again and took a breath. 'There was also my father's diet.' Red-faced, I told the psychiatrist about the strict regime I had devised for my father. It felt so damning that I failed to tell him it had been a first.

I finished speaking and sat back, drained.

'That's quite a story.' The psychiatrist looked down at his notes for a moment. The room was silent. I could not have felt more naked if I'd taken my clothes off. I had taken our lives apart piece by piece to show this man. But that was how the process worked, wasn't it? Now the psychiatrist knew the whole sorry story, perhaps he would be able to help us. Help Riche.

The psychiatrist looked back up, held my gaze, his expression serious.

Then: 'Is there anything else I should know?'

The question took me aback. What more could I say?

He waited, not taking his eyes off me, and I knew I was missing something. I cast my mind back over my reading. What did the books say were the other risk factors for anorexia? I felt we'd covered diet fetishes and family discord...

'Are you asking me if someone has sexually abused Riche?'

He raised an eyebrow. 'Is that a possibility?'

'No,' I said. 'If anything, we've over-protected our children. We used the same babysitters all the time and the children seemed happy to see them.'

The psychiatrist didn't say a word, just looked at me, his expression carefully neutral. Suddenly I saw where he was headed.

'Kevin?' I gasped. 'You've got to be kidding.' I would have laughed if I'd had enough breath in my body. 'Kevin's just insensitive. He's not a *monster*.'

It felt as if the walls were collapsing in on me, realising I'd just bared my soul to someone who was prepared to believe the worst of a man he'd never met on the grounds that his son had anorexia. This was the very worst incarnation of the parents-are-to-blame theory.

A lump in my throat made swallowing difficult; the room was too hot. I rolled up my sleeves. It would never have crossed my mind to suspect Kevin of this unspeakable act, and his relationship with Riche stood up to the most intense scrutiny of hindsight. Riche had no history of bedwetting or unexplained tears, and he had never displayed any reluctance to be left with Kevin prior to the dispute over his grandmother. There'd been no sign of discord at all until this argument. Besides, the hours Kevin worked he was rarely alone with me, let alone any of the kids.

This was a whole new level of suspicion, of possible condemnation, I hadn't expected to encounter. It occurred to me that the medical profession, which could easily get a bee in its bonnet about such things, might prove to be more of an adversary in this than even I had feared.

'I'd like to speak to Riche.' The psychiatrist was all business. 'Alone. Can you ask him to come in?'

I opened the door and went out into the corridor. Riche was still pacing, his steps fast and cautious as if he expected the floor to open up and swallow him.

'The doctor wants to talk to you,' I said to my son. 'I'll wait right here.'

'Don't make me go in by myself, Mum. Please.' His face anguished.

I turned to the doctor. 'Riche wants me with him.' Without waiting for a reply, I walked back in and sat down. Riche followed hesitantly.

His eyes flitted around the room, searching for latent threats, and he fidgeted anxiously. When the psychiatrist asked him what had been going on, he refused to answer. He shot me a look of reproach and kept his mouth shut. All up, the interview lasted one minute.

'Okay,' the psychiatrist said. 'I need to examine you. Can you get up on the couch?'

Riche didn't move.

'He can't.' I felt suddenly tired. I explained Riche's fear of contamination by calories left by other patients. My explanation proved worthy of a note.

'I'll manage with you standing.' He reached for Riche, who backed away.

'The doctor washed his hands after the last patient,' I said to Riche. 'See, there's a hand basin next to the couch. And he has no food in here.'

Riche stuck a hand out to have his pulse measured. The psychiatrist jotted down a number and then reached into his pocket for his stethoscope.

Riche stared at it, as if it were radioactive. 'He's not touching me with that thing.'

The psychiatrist looked to me for guidance. I shrugged.

'I'll only use it to check your blood pressure,' the psychiatrist said. 'I won't put it on your chest.'

Riche stiffened but complied.

'Can you open your mouth? I want to see how moist your tongue is.'

Riche poked out a dry, white-coated tongue.

The psychiatrist made another quick note and turned to me. 'Richard's very sick. He's dehydrated, he's wasted, and his pulse is weak. He needs to be in hospital.'

No; not now. We were making good progress, I nearly had him on high ground.

The air around me felt very still. I imagined Riche held down, screaming. A room full of strangers. Bright lights. Blood tests.

Medical instruments. A tube down his gullet, his hands tied to the bed to stop him pulling it out.

'Is he in danger if I don't agree?'

'I can't guarantee his safety. He could have a sudden cardiac arrest. That's difficult to predict.'

'Where would you send him?'

'The Mater Private.'

'When?'

'Tonight.'

The adrenaline surged. I edged forward in my seat as Riche's voice, low and urgent, broke the silence.

'You promised me, Mum. I can't go to hospital.'

I didn't reply. I kept my eyes on the psychiatrist. 'How long would he need to stay in?'

'I can't say.'

The jaws of the trap yawned.

'Can you give me some time to think about it?'

The psychiatrist paused. 'All right, but don't take too long. Make an appointment to see me again in a couple of days.'

'I will,' I said. I opened the door and let Riche out before me.

'I'm not going to hospital,' he said. 'I'll kill myself.'

'Trust me,' I said. I went in to the receptionist.

She put the phone down as I walked in. 'That was the doctor. He wants to see you the day after tomorrow.'

For the second time, I cited my rights as a healthcare consumer to a second opinion and said I'd call if we needed another appointment. I knew the psychiatrist's desire to admit Riche was completely reasonable considering Riche's condition, but I also believed I could turn the situation around soon. I handed over my credit card, signed the chit without so much as a glance at the figures, and hurried out to my son.

'Let's go home.'

I waited until we were well away from the psychiatrist's office before I added, 'We won't be seeing him again.'

'Thanks.' He didn't need to say anything more: his face said it for him.

○

I wondered if the psychiatrist would believe my second-opinion ploy. Strictly speaking, I was telling the truth. But I wouldn't be seeking any second opinions until I'd managed somehow to increase Riche's water consumption. If the psychiatrist didn't believe me, I might find child protection agents knocking on my door, but I'd cope with that if and when it happened.

Bone weary, I steered the car down Milton Road towards the motel. I'd publicly catalogued my faults—and Kevin's—in a way most parents never needed to. Wasn't that necessary with such a sick child? But, away from the seductive authority of the hospital, even I could see that it was pretty difficult to draw a straight connection between any one item on my list and my child's illness. Children survived greater traumas without succumbing to anorexia, and I felt more certain than ever that the archaeological dig was pointless.

Blame, causes, explanations—whatever word you wanted to apply to the reason for the car crash of Riche's health, all that was irrelevant for now. Chasing down the reckless driver wouldn't help a man with a car on his leg. The time for that would come later. The immediate task was to correct Riche's dehydration and to restore his nutrition.

Back at the motel, the smell of someone's dinner filled the concrete stairwell. My mouth watered and I realised I was hungry. And tired. And sick of Riche's anorexia.

I opened the door to a dark apartment with a refrigerator that contained little other than protein shakes and fruit and a bottle of chardonnay hidden in the vegetable drawer. I switched on the light and stood back for Riche. He must have sensed a confrontation looming because he kept a wary eye on me while I shut the apartment door behind us.

'You heard the psychiatrist. Dehydration might kill you. You have to drink more water.' I tried to sound like I was the one in the driving seat.

'I can't.' His voice quiet, hopeless. He looked at me through lowered eyes and twisted his hands together.

I was ready to hand over the car keys. This wasn't Riche's fault. He wasn't doing this to make my life difficult. But then I imagined his lifeless body in my arms. I marched over to the sink, took a glass from the dish drainer, and filled it from the tap. Tears welled up in his eyes as I walked back and held the glass out to him.

'Drink this!' Back behind the wheel.

Riche's voice came out in a whisper. 'I've already had some.'

'A few mouthfuls? Not enough.' More steel in my voice. 'Drink up.'

'I can't. It'll make me fat.'

I tilted the glass and looked at the water—colourless, calorie-free, guaranteed to slake the thirst Riche undoubtedly felt.

'It's *water*, for God's sake.'

Frustration made my voice louder than I had intended. On a family holiday three years ago, he and Andy and Louise had drunk the resort out of orange and mango mineral water. When a rainstorm appeared out of nowhere Riche and a friend stripped to their swimmers and splashed their bikes through the puddles. Then they tired of that, abandoned their bikes and lathered mud all over their bare skin. Riche looked like a Dickensian street urchin with his long legs, his lean but muscular body, his toothy grin. Now I couldn't get a drop of water past his lips and he had the wasted, hopeless look of a prisoner of war.

'How can anyone with your intelligence believe water will make you fat? Are you kidding me?'

Riche's trembling bottom lip, the tears in his eyes, and the tense way he held his body told me the answer to that. I had never heard of someone with anorexia refusing water because they thought it would make them fat. My hands shook.

He was waiting for my next move. Neither the therapist nor the dietician had given me any advice on how to make Riche drink, but I had heard them talking to him about his 'negative mind'. Admittedly they hadn't had much success altering his behaviour as yet, but it was worth a shot.

'You're listening to your negative mind,' I said. 'Trust me instead. I'm your mother. I wouldn't do anything to hurt you.' I felt like a wolf dressed up as a mother.

But my words had no effect in any case. I didn't understand that when I confronted Riche's anorexia by trying to force him to eat or drink, the anorexic voice in his head grew so loud it drowned out his voice of reason. And if he heard my voice at all, he heard it as a whisper.

Riche clamped his lips together, and a tear rolled down his cheek. I lifted a finger and brushed it away. He whimpered at my touch and ran to the bathroom to wash off the calories I might have transmitted.

While he was in there I rang Jan Cullis and told her that, despite the psychiatrist's threat of hospitalisation, Riche still refused to drink.

Jan sighed. 'It's always the same,' she said. 'Bring Riche to my place and I'll see what I can do.'

I told Riche we were going to see Jan. 'This isn't a choice,' I said. 'Come downstairs with me and get in the car.'

I expected Riche to object but he did as I asked. As always when calories and imagined calories weren't directly involved, he showed a heart-rending desire to please me.

The sun had set by the time I parked outside Jan's apartment block, but the late summer air felt warm and feathery on my skin. I glanced at my watch: 8 pm. I doubted I could find this kind of help anywhere else in Australia.

Jan let us into her apartment and we followed her into the living-room. It was separated by a bench from the kitchen, which Riche turned to face much as one would face an angry bear. With his back to the wall and his eyes on the bench, he scuttled sideways into the livingroom. Jan introduced us to her daughter, Sam, who was visiting from Melbourne, and then offered us a seat. I sat on the sofa and smiled at Sam as Riche hovered in front of me.

'Sam's a doctor,' Jan told Riche. 'She'll explain why you need to drink water.'

Sam gave Riche an earnest look. 'You can't live without water,' she said. She sat with her legs curled under her, long dark hair pulled back in an efficient ponytail. That was me once, a young and confident professional. Before children, before anorexia.

'You need it to make blood, and blood carries oxygen to your brain.

Your kidneys need water to clear waste from your body. Your brain sits in watery fluid.'

Jan took a bottle of water from her refrigerator and filled a glass. She took it over to Riche. 'You need to drink this,' she said. 'I promise it won't make you fat.'

'You eat meat.' Riche spat the words out, his voice full of loathing. 'And you've got other bad things in your fridge.'

The refrigerator was behind the enemy lines, its contents hidden from Riche, but I guessed he knew from Jan's conversations at Footprints of Angels that she dabbled in the dark arts of meat and dairy.

Jan thought for a moment. 'You know what? We'll buy some fresh bottled water. The supermarket over the road keeps it separate from the food. I'll send Sam.'

Sam returned ten minutes later with several bottles—different brands. Jan offered one to Riche.

'Here,' she said. 'You saw Sam bring this in. It hasn't been anywhere near our fridge. The water is clean and it's calorie-free.'

Riche shook his head. 'No,' he said. 'It'll make me fat.' He gave me the kind of look you might see on the face of a homeless person begging for food. 'Take me home. Please.'

'You have to drink,' Jan said. 'Or I'll call the ambulance. If you don't drink in hospital you'll get an IV drip, and if you don't eat you'll get a nasogastric tube.'

Riche pressed his fingertips to his forehead. He huddled over and made ugly choking sounds as sobs shook his body. The air conditioning seemed to make not a jot of difference—I was sweating. Riche turned a tear-streaked face to me.

'Don't let her call an ambulance.' His voice was thick with tears, his face flushed. He held out his hands, palms upturned, and screwed up his face. '*Please!*'

'I'm so sorry.' The process would be torture for Riche. Manhandled by strangers, wheeled into an ambulance and wired up to machinery that had been wired up to other, possibly fat, people; rushed to hospital to face more of the same. My tears fell freely.

If I'd owned a futuroscope along with my retrospectoscope, I would have read in *Help Your Teenager Beat an Eating Disorder* by James Lock and Daniel Le Grange that a parent's anxiety can be interpreted as wavering by an anorexic child. This in turn may increase the child's resistance. But that book wasn't yet published when I sat in Jan's livingroom, every muscle in my body taut, and wept. I was unaware of the mixed signals I was sending my son through my distress.

His breath came in ragged gasps. His head swung from side to side, his eyes glinting. Suddenly he lunged for the balcony. Jan anticipated his move, ran to the door, slammed it shut and slid the bolt across. Riche turned and made a dash for the front door. Jan dodged the coffee table and blocked his way.

'Come on Riche,' she said. 'Drink the water.' She picked up the telephone and started to dial.

'No, wait,' I said. In calling Riche's bluff Jan may have underestimated his fear of fat. Ambulance officers might be enemy foot soldiers, but water was a nuclear warhead. He would refuse to drink. Jan would have to follow through with her threat. Riche would see this as my betrayal. I would lose his trust. Besides, the escalating drama in the room frightened me. Would the stress prove too much for Riche's weakened heart? Mine felt like it might buckle under the strain of seeing him so distraught.

'I'm going to take Riche home,' I said. 'I'll keep trying.'

Jan must have had some faith in my ability to get Riche to drink water—I had succeeded with the protein shakes after all—so she handed over the bottles and followed us to my car. She watched as if it were the most normal activity in the world while I cleared the back seat of potential contaminants, put the bottles down and then launched into the door and seatbelt rigmarole. After several weeks of practice, I managed this without breaking into a sweat.

Jan hugged me. 'Call me if you need me.'

'Thanks.' I meant it. Jan hadn't been able to get Riche to drink, but she had shown me I wasn't alone. For that I would always be grateful.

○

Riche looked fragile and exhausted in the stark light of our apartment. As he waited for me to speak I experienced a moment of pure despair. I thought he would die, and die soon, and in my state of heightened emotion and exhaustion, I thought I would prefer that to seeing him suffer for years in hospital like Jan's daughter Bronte. Death was not the worst thing that could happen to a person.

Nor was prison.

'Do you realise I will be jailed when you die?' Riche was unable to drink to save himself. Would he do it to save me? It was my last roll of the dice. 'Because you will. Nothing's surer.'

Riche's eyes widened. 'Give me a bottle.'

I picked the bottle with a plastic seal over the lid. *The Original Adam's Ale* said the label. *Pure Australian water*. I made a show of breaking and removing the plastic seal: no bugs in this bottle. Riche held it at arm's length and made a reciprocal show of checking it. He examined the bottle from several angles, took a good long look at the opening, and read the label. Finally, he took a deep breath, closed his eyes, raised the bottle to his lips, and drank half. He paused to catch his breath, and then he drained the remainder of the 250 millilitres of water. He handed back the empty bottle.

'I'm scared,' he said. 'It's going to make me fat.'

I fought the urge to hold him and repeated my worn-out mantra: 'Trust me, I'm your mother. I wouldn't hurt you.' Words not even I believed.

I listened to him in the bathroom. He spat a few times after he cleaned his teeth; he didn't vomit. When he came out, he asked me again if the water would make him fat. Again, I reassured him. An hour later, I was still reassuring him that the water wouldn't add so much as an ounce of fat to his body. And no I wasn't tricking him. And yes my hands were clean when I touched the bottle. And no the bottle didn't get near any food in the supermarket. And how did I know that? I knew because I'd been to the supermarket a million times. And no, I would never, ever tell him a lie.

○

After Riche fell asleep I sat at the table, hunched over a glass of chardonnay. I took a mouthful of the wine and while I swilled the cool, soothing liquid around my mouth I wondered idly how many calories it contained. Plenty, I hoped. The motel reception was closed for the evening so I couldn't buy a frozen dinner from its limited pantry. Apart from the wine, I had fruit or a choice of cans: baked beans or tuna. I topped up my glass and let myself sink into self-pity. This might be my next five to seven years—an endless, exhausting fight. My head throbbed and my body ached. I stared into the glass, too despairing to read, or even to go to bed. I might have sat there in a stupor all night if the phone hadn't rung.

'How was your day?' Kevin sounded cheerful.

The picture of my weeping son was fresh in my mind, and I could barely bring myself to speak to my husband.

'How do you think?' God, I sounded like a witch. I tried again. 'How are you?'

'Busy.' Kevin's standard reply. 'We've been given a mandate to raise a billion dollars.'

The brown brick walls and the beige drapes closed in on my beige life and I felt myself snap. 'Who gives a fuck?' Who was this man, in his pinstriped suit and silver cufflinks, throwing ridiculous sums of money into the conversation while his starving son slept with tear-damp cheeks?

134

'Sorry,' Kevin said. 'I never know what to say. You sound strung out. Tough day?'

I told him; it sounded dull even to me.

'How much did you get him to drink?'

'250 millilitres.' I could hear my voice getting sharper. What did he care? Numbers just meant dollars to him.

'Great,' he said.

'Yeah, just great.' More of his annoying positive spin. 'Great' would be serving up dinner in the chaos of children and dogs at home in Mullumbimby. 'Great' would be Riche drinking gulps of juice, in between untidy mouthfuls of food. 'Great' was not a three-hour struggle over half a pint of water.

'You really think all this is my fault?'

'You can never take responsibility for your actions, can you?'

And I was away. Off on my high horse, and there was no reining me in.

The thing was, there had always been a competitive element to our marriage. It was part of what made us work; what gave us our edge. The thought of admitting to Kevin that I thought I might have failed in my specialisation, my primary role of parenting, stuck in my craw. Not for the first time, I turned it around and suggested Kevin see a therapist. 'For Riche's sake.'

'I've made an appointment to see the Merrill Lynch psychologist,' he said.

'He won't understand anorexia. And you won't discuss anything too personal.'

'I can't see anyone else.' Kevin's voice cracked. 'I'm running around like an idiot as it is.'

There was an instant in which I wished I could hug my husband. He, too, must hate seeing Riche suffer. And he was right. Between those meaningless billion-dollar deals and our other two children, to say nothing of my sick mother and ageing father, and the animals I had accumulated, Kevin didn't have a spare couple of hours to bare his soul to a therapist. At least the psychologist employed by Merrill Lynch was close at hand. I made a murmuring noise to show my understanding.

Kevin was adept at hiding his emotions; assuming he didn't have them was a mistake I made too often.

A memory surfaces of Riche, maybe four years old, blowing bubbles and squealing with delight at the glistening rainbow-coloured apparitions. Was he wearing his miniature NASA space suit or sweating in synthetic Batman? I don't remember, but I do remember his glittering Roald Dahl eyes and exuberant movements as he chased down those bubbles under the wisteria behind our house. And I remember him gaping, slack-jawed, as the bubbles burst on the cobblestones and it was as if they had never existed.

Riche's obsessive refusal to drink water reminded me of those bubbles. Within a week of drinking the first bottle of The Original Adam's Ale, Riche had switched to obsessively consuming two 250 ml bottles a day and all that remained of weeks of struggle were ghost-like memories. With each bottle, I broke the seal on the lid, handed him the bottle, and vouched for its purity. Although he still looked like a third-world refugee, his tongue was moist and his skin had lost its dry, papery look.

The results from his blood test a few days later were neither better nor worse. The following Friday, I took Riche to the laboratory technician for another blood test to confirm that his blood electrolytes had stabilised.

'Such beautiful blue eyes, and would you look at those lashes?' Trish said, her Irish accent charming my son, as it always did. 'Will you marry me when you grow up?'

To get to Trish we had to pass a coffee shop, with its bristling arsenal of calories, and survive a white-knuckle elevator ride that might potentially trap us with someone else's food. But she was a deadly sniper with a syringe, and Riche rewarded her by yielding precious millilitres of blood.

After the test came my regular Friday evening vigil on the bench outside Games Workshop. This weekend I planned to spend as much time as possible there until Kevin, Andy and Louise arrived on Saturday afternoon. I flicked through magazines and watched the sneaker-footed teens and family groups wander into the Rebel Sports store opposite. Every so often the manager would emerge and glare in the direction of Games Workshop, affronted by the happy sound of war games. A Games Workshop staffer told me their manager used noise complaints to rate staff performance: three complaints in one night earned them a carton of beer. Two uninterrupted hours on the bench outside earned them my gratitude.

Riche would happily have lived at Games Workshop; it was the one place where he seemed released a little from the strictures of his illness, where a shy smile might occasionally grace his face. Each game lasted anywhere between forty minutes and three hours and there were a number of different games including Warhammer, Warhammer 40,000, Lord of the Rings, Warhammer Skirmish and Warhammer Mordheim. Riche's favourites were Warhammer and Mordheim—both, Andy would later explain to me, more complex than the other games.

Riche liked Friday nights the best because that was when Sean ran the game, using store armies. Normally two or three boys, each with sovereign rule, versed their armies. But with Sean at the helm, participants formed two teams. Within each team, each person controlled a single unit of an army. These raucous games were apparently less tactical, more of a free-for-all. On this night, as on other nights, I kept an eye on Riche from the safe distance of the bench, not wanting to intrude. Whenever I checked on him, he looked totally engaged. He flicked his hair back off his face and timidly added his voice to the others when cheering broke out. But he kept his distance physically, and I noticed that he didn't touch any of the pieces himself.

When the night's hostilities had finished I collected him and we headed through Myers' department store to the carpark. Back at the motel I gave him his fruit plate and waited until he was asleep before I ducked down to the office to buy a frozen microwave dinner. I was savouring a mouthful of chicken smothered in a gluey sauce when the telephone rang. It was Dr C, the doctor from Walton Bridge Medical Centre who had referred us to the psychiatrist and was monitoring Riche's blood chemistry.

On a Friday night? My heart shifted a few gears and my armpits felt damp.

'There's a problem with Riche's blood test.' She was hard to hear over the laughter and car horns in the background. 'I tried to call you earlier. His potassium is high. It's 6.5. It could be a lab error, but I'm worried because I don't know what's in that protein powder.'

My medical training deserted me and I reverted to a primitive superstitious reflex. This was payback time. Riche was going to die because I refused to have him admitted to hospital. I dismissed the (more likely) possibility of a laboratory error and pictured Riche's eyes rolling back in his head as he keeled over. He really could die if his potassium were that high. And for all Dr C and I knew the powder could have been loaded with potassium. To make matters worse, without discussing it with the dietician I had added extra powder to Riche's shakes that week. Not much; but maybe, I thought, enough to cause a problem. A potassium of 6.5 could alter Riche's cardiac rhythm in a body with precious little margin for error. Internal chemical warfare.

I don't know why I hadn't insisted on knowing the composition of the powder. If Riche had been diagnosed with cancer I would never have agreed to chemotherapy without knowing what drugs were to be used. If he had come down with pneumonia I would have had nothing to do with unlabelled antibiotics. But the therapists thought it best to keep such information from clients. And I, frantic with worry and grateful to have found help that didn't involve hospital, had simply acquiesced.

'I'll ring the children's hospital and call you back,' Dr C said.

I ran into Riche's bedroom to see if he had died in his sleep. The rapid shallow rise of his chest reassured me. Back in the kitchen, I scraped my chicken casserole into a plastic bag and knotted it tightly before I threw it in the rubbish, then opened the door and windows and flapped my hands to disperse the smell. Television sounds drifted in from neighbouring apartments, along with the low hum of conversation. The occasional laugh. I envied Kevin. I imagined him asleep in bed after having dinner with our other two children, the two who didn't think sitting down to a meal was the worst thing that could ever happen to a person.

Dr C rang back. 'The emergency registrar at the children's hospital said if you take Riche in, she'll repeat the test straight away. You'll have the results back in half an hour. Of course if Riche's potassium really is that high, he'll have to stay and be monitored.'

Here it was: the emergency I'd dreaded. So much for my promise. I wasn't about to let my son die. 'How will I talk Riche into going to the emergency department?'

'I don't know,' she said. 'But if he won't go, call the ambulance.'

The usual nightmare images of restraints and syringes flashed through my mind, but I would do it if necessary. I wasn't going to lose my son.

Desperate for help, I dialled the mobile number of Riche's therapist. Nothing. I found out later that all the staff from Footprints of Angels had gone out to dinner and switched to voicemail. I slammed the phone down; Riche's blood could be delivering fatal doses of potassium to his heart while I wasted time on unanswered calls. I grabbed my purse and keys and went into his bedroom.

'Riche, wake up.' I gripped the keys, the metal digging into my flesh.

Riche's long eyelashes fluttered, and his deep blue eyes gazed up at me from under a wrinkled brow.

'There's a problem with today's blood test,' I said. 'We have to go to the hospital to have it done again.'

'I'm too tired,' Riche said. He rolled over to face the wall.

'Come on, Dr C's arranged it. It won't take long.'

Yawning and rubbing his eyes with the back of a hand, Riche swung his skin-and-bone legs off the bed. He slid his feet into his scuffed leather sandals and stood up, fully dressed. He never explained why he refused to wear his pyjamas, but I assumed it was because they implied relaxation. Riche could never allow himself to let down his guard.

I held the front door open and Riche stumbled through, a whisper of life breathed into a swollen-headed stick figure. He followed me down the stairs into the kind of sticky subtropical night that would, no doubt, have encouraged people all over Brisbane to throw some steak on a barbecue and open a few beers. We went through the car routine with no objection from Riche and, as we sped along the motorway, I chattered to distract him. *I promise I won't put you in hospital,* I had said.

The Royal Children's Hospital carpark was a cold cement cavern with shadowy corners beyond reach of the fluorescent lighting, nearly empty at this hour. *First, do no harm.* Part of the Hippocratic Oath. Would the emergency doctors understand anorexia? Would they know that to admit Riche to hospital, unless absolutely necessary, would be to harm him?

The woman at the reception desk of the emergency department, an uninterested blur of plump cheeks and permed hair, listened as I explained our situation.

'Do you have a Medicare card?' She took the card I held out and shuffled through some Post-it notes. 'No, that doctor went off duty fifteen minutes ago. The other registrar's busy right now. You'll have to wait.'

I checked the waiting room: a family with a pale, sick-looking baby waited on one side, some young children jiggled the drinks machine on the far wall. Another group huddled miserably on the middle island of chairs. It was a far cry from the adult emergency departments where I had worked. On weekends, they were crowded with injured footballers and aggressive drunks, as well as crash victims and sweating middle-aged men clutching their chests. Patients sometimes waited hours to be seen. With luck, we'd be back in the car in less than an hour. I settled myself in a plastic chair while Riche paced.

'Sit down,' I said. 'You need to rest. This chair is clean.'

'I'm not sitting on those chairs.' He shot a hostile look to the right—an empty crisp packet and drink can I had missed further along the row. The airconditioned chill had turned his lips blue and goosebumps stood up on his bare arms; he only ever wore a T-shirt, not trusting the new sweater I had bought him.

Time passed. The sick baby was called in with its anxious parents. Sick babies needed prompt attention, I knew that, but surely there was someone to look after *my* son. He looked pale and tired and on the verge of collapse. Couldn't a nurse show us to a cubicle? I'd stand a fighting chance of talking Riche into sitting on the edge of a bed, newly decontaminated with a freshly washed sheet.

Doors banged. Trolleys came and went. The baby was being admitted. Dr C had asked for the registrar to take Riche's blood— they were the senior doctors on in emergency in the evenings—but by now I would have happily let a new intern loose on Riche's arm. It was midnight and we'd been waiting an hour. An hour's worth of burned energy.

'Can't we go to the lab tomorrow?' Riche said. 'I feel okay. I don't feel any different.'

'You wouldn't,' I said. 'Not until it's too late and your heart goes into a dangerous rhythm.' I paused to control my ragged voice. 'I can't lose you.'

Riche abruptly ceased his pacing and stared at me, open-mouthed. I realised then that he didn't see death as a natural outcome of his behaviour. It was a completely novel thought and it scared him as much as it scared me.

It didn't stop him resuming his pacing, though. The minutes dragged by.

At one o'clock I marched up to the reception desk. 'Excuse me,' I said in a conciliatory voice. I waited for the receptionist to look up. 'My son has been standing for the last two hours because his anorexia makes him think the seats are contaminated. Can a doctor see him soon?'

'Shouldn't be long, dear,' the receptionist said in a heard-it-all-before voice. Her mouth hovered between a smile and a grimace, and she turned to her work. I wandered back to the waiting room and sat in silence. Riche continued his endless pacing.

I dislike hospitals. This was only the second time I had been in one with Riche other than for blood tests and the visit to the psychiatrist. The first was twelve years previously in New York City when Riche was born. In the early stages of labour, Kevin and I walked the streets near our apartment on Eighty-third and Broadway in an attempt to speed things up. We dodged panhandlers and ignored the curious glances of the Saturday evening crowds. Later, cars honked impatiently as I lowered myself into a taxicab to go to New York Hospital, where Riche was born at 7.53 am on an April morning. We named him Richard Samuel. His middle name in recognition of his US citizenship. Richard for his godfather and also, in a fanciful moment, after a crusading king, Richard the Lionheart. Riche informed us years later that the crusaders were murderers and rapists. History, like memory, depends on perspective.

After Riche's birth, the nurses wheeled us both to a tiny room overlooking the East River, one of the few rooms with the combined benefits of a view and a spartan ensuite. Jackie Kennedy had roomed there after her children's births, or so the nurses told us, and a quick inspection suggested that the room had been preserved in its original state. Riche lay in a crib alongside my hospital bed, and a trundle bed was squeezed in for Kevin. When the nursing staff took Riche to the nursery during the official rest period, I wept inconsolably until my obstetrician intervened, and Riche was returned to me. He settled into my arms, latched onto my breast, and opened his eyes. They were the colour of the ocean back home in Australia.

I looked at my watch. We had spent three hours in this Brisbane emergency room. Riche had spent the entire time standing or pacing.

'I'm cold,' he said. 'Can't we go home?'

I strode over to the receptionist. 'My son's freezing,' I said, all attempt at conciliation abandoned. 'If no one's going to see him, we might as well go home.'

'Hang on.' The receptionist walked through a door behind her desk and returned with a nurse.

We followed her down a corridor into a curtained cubicle with a freshly made-up stretcher trolley, a metal table and a sad-looking Thomas the Tank Engine poster tacked to the wall. Riche scrutinised the conspicuously clean sheets before leaning against the bed. 'I hate Thomas the Tank Engine.'

'You loved him when you were young. Remember your Brio train set?'

'That was the old me,' Riche said. 'The bad me.'

'What?'

With all that we were going through, something like that could still make me feel as if the bottom had fallen out of my stomach.

'I was bad,' Riche repeated.

I thought furiously for some way to derail this conversation. 'How do you think this wall should be decorated?'

'They should build an ant farm into the wall,' he said. 'Then there'd always be something interesting to watch.'

We were finalising the ant farm design when the curtain was pulled back and a young doctor introduced himself. He had a heavy Asian accent which I was unable to place. I wondered if he'd graduated in a country where people starved because of food shortages, rather than this bizarre illness.

'Sorry about the wait,' he said.

'So am I,' I said.

'You need a blood test?'

Riche nodded. The doctor tightened a tourniquet around his arm and asked him to make a fist. Riche was cold and had eaten and drunk nothing in the hours we had waited, with the result that his blood vessels had contracted. The doctor probed with the needle while Riche squirmed and cried out. When the needle finally hit a vein, it took a long time for the syringe to fill. Sweat beaded Riche's forehead and his face, always pale, became ashen. The doctor had left the specimen tubes too far away; when he stretched to reach for them he wriggled the needle. Riche winced. The doctor filled his tubes and withdrew the needle before he released the tourniquet, a mistake that would guarantee a decent bruise. Then he took his tubes, and left Riche and me to exhaust the topic of ant farms.

Shortly before 3 am the test results came back: Riche's potassium was 4.1—within normal range. Probably the original sample had been shaken at some point, releasing potassium from inside the blood cells to cause a false high blood level. (And in fact, in these early days of having the protein shakes a more likely complication would have been a low potassium level, as part of the refeeding syndrome. But I was yet to learn this.)

Riche smiled and chatted to me as we left the hospital, looking as if he had won the lottery. We returned to our apartment where we snatched one and a half hours sleep before Riche woke me for the first shake of the day. They were getting earlier and earlier—we were starting at 5 am by now. Anorexic obsessiveness makes no exceptions for late nights.

○

Later I took Riche to the Roma Street Parklands. We strolled in the dreamlike state of exhaustion through the formal gardens, past beds of violent purple and pink petunias and under a creeper-covered arbour. A gardener was pulling out some straggly impatiens in preparation for autumn replanting. We stopped at the man-made waterfall in the centre of the garden and Riche stared at the water for a few moments.

'It's your fault I can't talk to Dad.' He sounded judicious; as if he were acknowledging an indisputable truth.

I thought he was joking.

'You left me at home with him after we saw that psychologist,' he continued. 'That's why we had the fight. If you hadn't left me with him, that wouldn't have happened.'

Later I would see the accusation as his starved brain's attempt to rationalise an unbearable situation. Not then. I felt as though I'd been knifed. I had no answer for him at all.

Have you ever counted the minutes in a week? The maths is simple: a couple of quick multiplications and an addition will give you 10,080 minutes. If your son wakes you at 5 am for his first protein shake, if your son's illness keeps him out of school for months at a stretch, if your son can no longer step on the space between the cracks, then he will find there is nothing quick about those minutes. I had no control over Riche's sleeping hours when, he told me, images of food taunted him. But I could help him fill the daylight hours.

Consequently, on a Thursday evening a week or so after the potassium crisis, we joined the endless river of brake lights stretching north towards the Brisbane Taoist Tai Chi Society. Joining these classes wasn't the smartest decision I had made to date—exercise had, after all, been part of Riche's weight-loss strategy—but I had become almost as obsessive in my pursuit of his happiness as he was about his dwindling size. In addition to these classes, I had racked up a $3,000 bill at Games Workshop, unwise kilometres in the botanic gardens and a library of fiction by David Eddings and Terry Pratchett that provided temporary asylum for my son in their fantastical landscapes. When anorexia has insinuated its lying, screeching voice into your son's head you will go to great lengths to drown it out.

But of course it wasn't just Riche who needed distraction. Left to its own devices, my mind filled with self-punishing thoughts derived from the books I had read. Bruch, Pipher, Levenkron: all those bookshelves of therapists pointing their collective finger at me. Better I submit to the discipline of a martial art.

○

Tyres squealed and horns blared as we drove down Lutwyche Road and Riche riffed on the ugliness of contemporary architecture—all concrete blocks and glass—to the staccato beat of his hand on his thigh. I ground my teeth; I'd heard it all before. When he had said all there was to say on this topic, he moved on to a perennial favourite: the evils of US military aggression, a personal affront to a boy who had once worn his American birth as a badge of pride.

I almost preferred the days when the thoughts in his head silenced him.

The traffic lights at the corner of Bradshaw Street were green, so I made a left and parked alongside the squat brick building where the classes were held and went round to open Riche's car door. He climbed out and waited for me to close the door.

I walked road-side of Riche, my biceps flexed, a full-back ready to head off a dash into the traffic should we encounter ground-level food. Riche paused at the corner and eyed the nearby Chinese restaurant, assessing, then sprinted the last few yards to the door of the building so as to minimise contact with airborne calories.

On our first Tai Chi visit, Riche had asked if the restaurant sold meat dishes—the evil double whammy that fattened people and enacted cruelty to animals. In line with my new policy of honesty when possible, I lied. The restaurant was vegetarian, I said: it specialised in tofu dishes, and wasn't it funny how Mongolian tofu smelled the same as Mongolian lamb? *Cross my brittle heart and hope he doesn't die.*

Upstairs, Riche stood near the front of the long, low-ceilinged room, creating a neutral zone of space and bodies between him and the hostile kitchen territory off the back of the room. The harsh lighting turned his face an oyster shade, the colour of the protein shakes. I took my position behind Riche and tried to clear my mind. No matter which way I looked, I could see my son in the mirrors that lined the walls.

The teacher, a tall heavyset man, rallied the class. We were an unlikely mix: a young businessman, some middle-aged housewives, three giggling secretaries, Riche and me. All seeking inner health and fitness or, in Riche's case, a decrease in body mass. And *ker-ching*: payday. Riche's face eased into the slightest of smiles as he turned to the teacher and waited for the first move.

We had learned over half of the 108 named sequences. Riche was first to master each new glide or turn. But the slow, controlled moves frustrated him: he knew he could burn more energy if he picked up the pace.

I took him aside during a class break. 'Tai Chi is a discipline. You've got to keep time with everyone else.'

Riche gave me a look that hinted at my stupidity. 'That's my natural rate. The others are slow because they don't know what they're doing.'

'Doesn't matter. Follow the instructor.'

After the break I watched to see if he had heeded my advice. He hadn't. While the class was 'Creeping Low Like a Snake' (sequence 75), Riche shot off to the right, doing the accelerated version of 'Go Back to Ward off Monkey' (sequence 78). With his rapid, jerky movements, he looked like a wind-up doll. And with each step, he made loud phutting sounds that betrayed the passing of wind. Those protein shakes packed a punch. One or two classmates looked in his direction. Most did a reasonable job of feigning deafness. Riche moved further ahead. I caught his eye in the mirror and mouthed the words, 'Slow down.' He ignored me.

If I had known our Tai Chi classes would end abruptly six weeks later, on the final evening of our beginners' course, I wouldn't have bothered with trying to restrain Riche.

On that evening, as we waited for the class to start, Riche moved abruptly into his 'Boy Poised to Flee Calories' sequence. This involved torso-twitching, feet-scuffing, hand-swatting and various unusual facial tics. I responded with my much-practised 'Mother on the Alert' sequence—rapid, shallow breathing and side-to-side scanning movements of the head—until I saw the graduation cake. And then I watched, biceps again flexed, for Riche's next move. *Stay!* But even as I silently begged him, he was by my side.

'I feel sick,' he said. 'Can we go home?'

The teacher accepted my apologies, gave us our navy blue graduation T-shirts with the white club logo, and offered us places in the intermediate class. I knew Riche's answer before I asked. The cake had permanently contaminated the room. I would have to find other ways to ward off the monkey.

We'd been in Brisbane for four weeks. Riche was now well hydrated and had not missed a single protein shake. The only unfinished shake was the one during our Mullumbimby visit. I didn't know if he'd gained any weight because, true to his word, the dietician didn't share this information with me. I guessed if he had, it was very little. The immediate risk of him collapsing in the street had passed, yet any thought of him tucking into a hearty meal seemed frankly delusional. The prediction Jan had made during our initial interview—five years or longer for recovery—was starting to look realistic: Riche would do anorexia instead of high school.

So be it. My shopping list now included: more permanent accommodation in Brisbane, a sympathetic psychiatrist, a paediatrician's sign-off on Riche's medical stability, and a supply of chardonnay to cushion my landing each evening once Riche was in bed.

My challenge was how to tell Kevin. We shared a financial history: he earned, I spent. And not just on food. I had a backlog of books to read at home and enough clothing to see me through to the end of the decade. Would my husband see a long-term rental as the latest example of my fiscal irresponsibility?

'I need to rent an apartment,' I said during our nightly sparring match.

'You mean sign a lease?'

'We'd start with a year.'

Kevin was silent, most likely engaged in mental arithmetic: $600 on therapy, $600 on a nanny for the other two children; and $800 for our motel apartment. We paid extra for accommodation for the rest of the family during weekend visits, as Riche couldn't cope with younger children 'who never wash their hands'. On top of that, although the initial anxiety-fuelled binge at Games Workshop had slowed, I still spent at least $200 each week on Warhammer models, the only thing that distracted Riche from his frightening thoughts, and one of the few remaining ways, once Tai Chi was axed, of filling in those 10,080 minutes. In all, over two thousand anorexia-related dollars each week. It was expenditure I viewed as non-negotiable, grateful we could afford it. Kevin, with his banker's hat firmly on his head, saw only an endless tidal wave of money surging in the wrong direction.

He broke his silence with an expletive. 'What will I have to fork out for that? Shut-up Minnie.' He paused as Minnie barked in the background. 'Your dog's hopeless. I wish you'd trained him.'

'It's a she.' I softened despite myself at Kevin's habitual and endearing pronoun confusion. 'I don't know the cost. I've yet to speak to an agent.'

'This illness could bankrupt us.' Another expletive. 'Guess my retirement's just been put on hold.'

We both lapsed into silence. Kevin was right. Our dreams of a patchouli-scented retirement were disappearing into the sunset nirvana. If we had agreed to hospitalise Riche, the government health-care system would have picked up the tab—a far heftier one. But much as Kevin complained about our expenses, I knew he wouldn't want Riche in hospitalised isolation for months on end. The telephone call ended on a tender note. After all, Kevin, like me, was navigating unaided in the dark.

○

A mother from Footprints of Angels suggested we try her daughter's psychiatrist. I scheduled an appointment for the following week. When the day arrived, we set off after the 5 am, 8 am and 11 am shakes, the tooth-brushing, the spitting, the hand-washing, the multiple toilet visits and the seatbelt routine.

Between the car and the doctor's office Riche maintained his usual level of surveillance. Within seconds, he detected an apple core bogey and, whimpering, took evasive action—this child, who after seeing *The Lion King* at the age of three, charged around the house, a human Simba, brandishing a plastic sword as he yelled, 'I laugh in the face of danger.'

'It won't hurt you,' I said. In her better days, my mother would have told me I sounded like a broken record. This entire year was a broken record.

We made it through fifty metres of enemy territory in under fifteen minutes. Not a record, but not bad. The reception area smelled of disinfectant. Straight-backed vinyl chairs stood against the walls. A typed notice advised, *No food or drink thank you* yet Richie was still unwilling to risk the chairs and reluctant to pass up the opportunity to burn a few calories in the corridor. Unable to stop him, I signed in with the receptionist, sat down, and sifted through the magazines on the table. I picked up a *National Geographic*.

A door opened and a bespectacled man in jeans and an open-necked shirt appeared. He introduced himself as the psychiatrist.

'I'll see Riche first,' he said.

Riche shot me a look of loathing, one more blunt and harmless arrow from his well-stocked quiver, but shambled meekly enough into the office. I settled back to read my magazine. Wailing sounds came from behind another closed door—the autistic association had its headquarters in the same building—and for the first time in quite a long time, I experienced a pang of empathy. I was still studying the *National Geographic* index when Dr S's door opened and Riche sloped out, followed by the psychiatrist. He asked me in.

'Don't be long,' Riche said. He had already resumed his laps of the corridor, seeming to hover, weightlessly, an inch or two above the floor.

Dr S gestured to a padded chair by the wall and sat in a leather chair opposite mine. No white coat and no desk-as-barrier.

'Why don't you tell me what's been going on with Riche?' he said.

Once more, I laid out the bones of our story. Dr S listened without taking notes. When I faltered, he prompted me with a question. When I reached Riche's argument with his nana, he frowned and shook his head.

'That's terrible.' He was sitting with his legs crossed, an intent expression on his face. 'Your husband is an adult. He should have stood up for Riche.'

I said I was concerned for Kevin's sake that we had no communication with his mother; Dr S assured me that some relationships are best left alone. At least for now.

'Seeing Riche, I understand why you want to keep him at home,' he continued. 'The hospital environment would cause constant panic attacks. But is your family doctor happy with this arrangement?'

'She's happy as long as a psychiatrist and a paediatrician agree to the plan.' I inched forward in my chair, poised, if necessary, to invoke my right to a second opinion on this second opinion.

Dr S nodded. 'I'm happy to support you,' he said. 'Riche will do better in an outpatient situation. I need to earn his trust, though. It'll take time. Riche must feel free to end the interview when he's had enough.'

I felt myself relax. This approach sounded good. Finally we had a supportive medical team in place, a family doctor and a psychiatrist.

Only the paediatrician to go. I thought for a moment. 'You mentioned panic attacks. What do you mean?'

The doctor nodded again. 'Whenever Riche is exposed to food or something he thinks is contaminated, his brain tells him he has to get away. If he can't, he will feel a very high level of discomfort. You should protect him from this feeling whenever possible.'

I mentioned a therapist who'd criticised the decision I'd made to keep meat out of our house. We had rights, she said, as if Riche were infringing our civil liberties.

'No, you were right. It won't be forever.' Dr S smiled encouragingly. 'Riche will get better. You need to keep him safe until then, and you need to make life as tolerable for him as you can.'

Without giving specifics, he talked about a patient he'd been seeing for years with severe obsessive-compulsive symptoms. 'He's coping with university now.'

Coping with university? The long-term implications of Riche's illness struck home with renewed force. My smart, articulate son might eventually 'cope' with university? If he were lucky? I pushed the thought aside.

'What about medication?' I said. 'Do you think he needs anti-depressants?'

'They're worth trying,' Dr S uncrossed his legs. He stood up and walked over to sit at his desk. 'They might help with his obsessive-compulsive symptoms. I'll give you a script for liquid Prozac. If you think the hand-washing and other obsessions are getting worse, start the medication.' Dr S handed me the script. 'I'll also give you a script for Zyprexa. It's an antipsychotic that comes in wafer form. Slip it under Riche's tongue to calm him if he ever becomes really agitated.'

I felt sick. Antipsychotics were pharmaceutical heavy artillery. I couldn't imagine giving them to Riche, but I took the script. The psychiatrist gave me his card with phone numbers for all hours and asked me to return in a fortnight. When I checked my watch,

I realised we'd talked for nearly fifty minutes. I left with my son, and the doctor's assurance that I could call him any time, and the scripts for mind-altering drugs and the sense that finally I had found someone I could trust, someone who understood Riche's illness, someone who would provide me with the support I needed so badly.

○

Searching for an apartment with Riche in tow proved difficult. He hated being ushered into strange rooms, haunted with ghost-like calories, and I didn't want to risk leaving him alone in the car or, worse still, on the footpath. One day Riche refused to enter the front door of the apartment we were to inspect.

'Riche has anorexia,' I said to the real estate agent when we were out of earshot. I ran my eyes over the kitchen cupboards. 'He doesn't mean to be rude.'

'That's terrible,' the woman said. 'It's unusual in boys isn't it?'

I shook my head. 'You'd be surprised. It's roughly twenty-five percent in his age group. More like ten percent for older kids of course,' I took a quick breath and ploughed on, 'although that figure's probably not accurate. Older males often present with gastrointestinal complaints because of how anorexia is seen as a female disease.'

Finally, I focused on the agent. Her eyes had glazed over and I realised I had overstepped the boundaries of polite conversation.

'Oh, I see. Do you think this place would suit him?'

I knew it wouldn't: two bedrooms side by side and a kitchen–living area. Riche would be imprisoned in his bedroom, unable to enter the livingroom because of its proximity to the kitchen. 'I'll let you know,' I said as we walked back out to the stairwell where Riche was waiting.

The real estate agent gave Riche a smile as ruthlessly bright as a fluorescent strip. 'And how did a nice young boy like you get anorexia?' she said.

The nice young boy lined me up in his sights and released one of his poison arrows before he started wordlessly down the stairs.

'I hope I didn't say the wrong thing,' the agent said.

We didn't take that apartment, we didn't use that agent again, and I didn't mention Riche's anorexia to any other agents.

Finally I found a two-storey townhouse with a garage beneath. Steps led up to the open-plan ground floor, which had a lounge area at the front and a kitchen area behind that opened out onto a pocket-sized courtyard. Opposite the kitchen, a wall with two horizontal slits screened a staircase to the first-floor master suite, two additional bedrooms and a bathroom, all a safe distance from the kitchen. Riche could use the spare bedroom to paint his Warhammer models. Our windows overlooked the lush neighbouring gardens: lawns, clumps of agapanthus and clivea and, of course, neatly clipped box hedges and fragrant gardenias. The suburb even had a beautiful name—St Lucia I hoped would turn out to be the patron saint of eating disorders. But that was not to be; her interest lies with eyes.

Kevin and I bickered over the cost but ultimately we knew our priorities were the same. I signed the lease and we moved in, glad to escape the contaminating influence of the cleaners at the motel apartment.

The following weekend Kevin brought Andy and Louise to Brisbane. They were staying in the motel since Riche was still too ill to share accommodation so we arranged to meet in the cafe next to Borders after I'd dropped Riche off for his Saturday morning session at Games Workshop.

The longing to see my other two children had become a physical pain, a bruise in my chest. When they walked into the coffee shop I hugged them each for a long moment, breathing in their scrubbed-clean scent, not wanting to let them go. Louise looked fine. Andy looked thin and anxious, as if he were constantly expecting me to disappear. Over drinks and cookies I listened while Louise repeated the story Kevin had made up for them in the car. I was impressed with his effort but I wasn't going to let him know. When Louise had finished, Andy tugged at my sleeve.

'Do you want to look at my diary?' He pulled an exercise book from his backpack and passed it to me.

The first entry was dated February 10: 'I now proklaim this diary open.' It continued happily for the first week or so. Then on February 24 he wrote: 'Hi Mum, got one step closer to depreshon today. Heavy work with maths-out-of-the-book. Weather rainy: the sandpit covered in water.'

Too young to spell depression. Old enough at ten to know how it felt.

By the time I reached the entry for February 27, I had to blink furiously to see the words through a film of tears: 'Hi Mum, I wish you were here to teach me. It's like jail ecsept at morning tea and lunch. And Louise wastes sand.' Poor Andy. He loved his sandpit, formerly a volleyball court. While I fought anorexia in Brisbane, Andy was creating imaginary worlds and battling demons in his pit.

I couldn't read any more. I closed the book and leaned over to squeeze Andy's shoulders. 'We'll talk about this later,' I said, and I meant it. But somehow I let it slip by. I could scarcely muster the energy to lift my coffee cup, and I had no solution for Andy's loneliness.

Over the weekend Kevin and I maintained the polite front of strangers. We had been married for almost twenty years, since I was twenty-three and he was twenty-five. I remembered how I had rewritten the traditional vows, scrapping the clause on obedience but keeping 'till death do us part'. It didn't occur to me to add 'or a child's illness tears us apart and blame erodes our relationship.'

○

I ticked the psychiatrist and the accommodation off my shopping list. Wine supplies were easy. This left one major item: the paediatrician.

The problem here was that in the six weeks since starting at the clinic Riche's weight (I'd extracted this information from the Angels dietician) had increased by only just under two kilograms, part of which could be attributed to better hydration.

To the naked eye Riche's weight looked unchanged. In time, I would learn that an acceptable weight gain during treatment varies between one and one and a half kilograms per week. In six weeks Riche should have gained between six and nine kilograms. Even without this knowledge I understood that two kilograms wasn't enough and, with the usual worry that a new doctor might want to admit Riche to hospital, I was procrastinating about lining up an appointment with a paediatrician.

In the meantime, I had added another item to the list—a kitten. Riche wouldn't allow anyone's touch, even Trisska's, but surely he needed to feel the warmth of another living creature. I thought perhaps he'd make an exception for a kitten if it didn't eat meat. He said yes.

The inside of the pet shop at Mount Gravatt shopping centre smelled of damp straw but a happy chorus of meows and yaps lured Riche through the door.

'Look!' he said, pointing to the rear of the shop.

A sleek grey kitten was grooming itself on a beam. It looked older than the kittens in the front window. It turned its head and regarded us with saucer-like green eyes. An identical grey kitten leapt onto the beam from behind a partition. It crouched low, tail whipping from side to side, and then tackled its mate. The squirming mass of grey fur fell to the floor.

A rare smile lit up Riche's face. 'I want one of *those*.'

Done deal.

The shop assistant told me the cats were Layanese, a fourth-generation Himalayan–Burmese cross. Of course they were. We couldn't possibly have lucked onto a pair of common tabbies. 'They're brothers,' she said. 'The last of the litter. We were hoping to find them a home together.' She tilted her head at us.

I thought of Andy back in his sandpit. Riche looked at me. I gave a wry smile. *To hell with our credit card bill.*

Riche named our new housemates Kaffran and Brin, after characters in *Gamut's Ghosts*, a Warhammer series. They would somehow remain uncontaminated in Riche's mind, even if it meant I had to cook their vegetables and fish myself.

○

I had just poured my first glass of the evening when Kevin rang. I settled myself in the swivel chair near the telephone. The kittens watched from the wooden platform at the top of their scratch post.

'We bought two kittens today.' I sipped my wine.

'Just what we need,' Kevin said, 'a few more animals to look after. Aren't three dogs, a rabbit and a bunch of guinea pigs enough? Actually I think one of the guinea pigs is pregnant. It's really fat.'

I flinched. 'You've got to stop saying that word.'

'What word?' Kevin sounded surprised. 'Did I say fuck?'

'*Fat*,' I hissed, my voice low. This word had the power of black magic; it could conjure illness in young minds. 'You said fat, and we can't use that word anymore.'

'Oh come on, it's not like Riche can hear me.'

'That's not the point,' I said. 'Loui or Andy might hear. Do you want three anorexic children?'

'Of course I don't,' Kevin said. 'But they're not going to get anorexia just because I call the guinea pig fat.'

'You said it again.' I took a few mouthfuls of chardonnay, hoping it would ease the hard knots of muscle tightening in long ropes down the back of my neck and between my shoulder blades. 'I asked you not to say that word.'

'Okay, okay. I hear you. I won't say the F-word again.' The impatient edge to Kevin's voice seemed to snag in my head: he thought I was being ridiculous. 'Do you think you need some sleep?'

'I'm not tired,' I said. 'Why do you always say things like that? You know it annoys me.'

'Sorry, sorry, sorry,' Kevin said. 'Only trying to help. You sound tired.'

'Well I'm not.'

We sat in silence, a lot more than 150 kilometres apart. One of the kittens uncurled itself and sprang down from the scratching post. It came over to me, arching its back while it rubbed against my leg. I put my wineglass down and stroked the soft fur, filled with longing, with the wish to fall asleep and wake up in our cottage. Minnie squashed up against me, and my children, all three of them, safe and well in bed, this nightmare banished.

I knew Kevin was right. I was taking it too far. I still believe that language can carry unintentional weight, that its sharp barbs can inflict enormous harm. But when I think back to that phone call, it's clear that I was as ensnared in obsessive thinking as my son. Riche's illness was the sorcerer, not a three-letter word uttered by my husband.

Eventually Kevin broke the silence. 'Why don't you bring Riche home in April so we can go to the Shearwater bush dance? We could use a night out. We'll take Andy and Louise with us. It's a family affair. You can leave Riche in bed.' A delicate pause. 'We might even get to make love later.'

Make love? Why the hell would I want to do that? If the effort required to top up my drink left me limp, the thought of showing my husband a good time was enough to send me into a coma. We hadn't had sex in at least three months, and I saw no reason to break the drought now. Couldn't the man masturbate? I forced myself not to wonder if our abstinence would push Kevin into another woman's arms. I had to focus on Riche. Nothing else mattered.

I gave a martyred sigh. 'And how's that going to work?' My mother was in respite care for a few weeks so my father could have a holiday. If we went to the bush dance Riche would be alone on our sixty-acre property. 'Who's going to look after Riche?'

'He'll be twelve years old by then. He'll be fine for a couple of hours, won't he?' Kevin said.

'He can't even go into his bedroom.' Staggered, I realised Kevin had forgotten Riche thought our cottage was contaminated. 'Besides, he shouldn't be left alone with his thoughts. Who knows what he'd end up doing to himself.'

'Well there goes that idea.'

Silence.

'What are you thinking?'

'Nothing,' I said. 'Are you bringing the kids to see me this weekend?'

'I can't,' Kevin said. 'Loui's been invited to a party. We'll come up the following weekend. Do we still have to stay in the motel?'

'Afraid so,' I said. 'But I think Riche is up to having you here during the day as long as you don't go upstairs.'

I left Kevin to tend to his guinea pig obstetric duties, hung up the phone and picked up the *Australian*. A few words leapt out at me—Taliban, al Qaeda—but I couldn't bring myself to read the articles. Regimes might have risen and fallen around the world and natural disasters might have killed thousands. Isolated and unaware in a world ruled by calories, all I could think about was the injustice of the life Riche and I shared.

○

Expecting sympathy, I relayed my conversation with Kevin to Jan at Footprints of Angels.

'You've got to look at it from Kevin's perspective,' she said. 'He wants a night out with his wife because he loves her.'

At the time I thought this was nonsense. Kevin just didn't want to risk my anger by partying without me. Besides, I was so angry with him for almost everything, why should I look at anything from his perspective? Doing billion-dollar deals looked like a game of Monopoly compared with the prospect of managing Riche's illness for the next five years.

Riche and I quickly established a routine founded on one simple principle: it was time for Riche's protein shake. It was always time for a protein shake. Their preparation, consumption and aftermath dominated our lives.

Making them required compliance with the Protein Shake Preparation Ordinance that Riche had developed over a matter of days. The steps were clearly stated.

Wash hands. Scrub bench. Wash hands. Open refrigerator door and remove soymilk and strawberries. (Door must be swung wide so that soymilk carton avoids contact with contaminated rubber strip on door edge.) Wash hands. Remove protein powder and blender from cupboard. Wash hands. Measure and blend ingredients. Wash hands. Serve. Wash hands.

These steps were necessary to prevent additional calories on hands or objects from insinuating themselves into the protein shakes. I would check the horizontal peepholes in the staircase wall before I began shake preparation. Riche had taken to perching on the stairs there, out of reach of stray calories but well positioned to peer through and see if any unorthodox moves were being made. I followed regulations at all times, even if he was nowhere to be seen: like the traffic police with their breathalysers, his anorexia knew the value of random checks.

'Have you got my shake, Mum?' Riche would call down to me from the top of the stairs.

'Right here,' and I'd pick up a cup and climb the stairs.

I have unusually long feet that culminate in a great toe of excessive proportions, so that the tread in many staircases is insufficiently deep for them. This was the case for me in the townhouse. My heel cantilevered off the step, and I relied on the muscles of my forefoot for traction. (Riche has inherited my big toe gene. Other genes I have gifted him that I was aware of at that time include those for oversized blue eyes, a head for figures, long femurs, unremarkable cheekbones, dental malocclusion, a predisposition to obsessive-compulsive behaviour and a melancholic disposition.)

I always counted the steps on my way up.

'One, two, three...' Slowly, to match the pace of my feet. I was in no hurry to reach the top. Riche, on the other hand, was prone to run up the stairs, for two reasons: to outrun any mobile calories in the kitchen and to maximise energy consumption. The illness that had invaded his brain and controlled his thoughts knew how to make every step a winner.

'Four.' This brought me level with the peepholes.

'Five, six, seven.' My bare feet made shushing sounds on the beige carpet. Small synthetic nubs scratched my skin. At this level, featureless white walls enclosed me on either side. The seventh step bore the first of the protein-shake stains that arced in a gentle curve to the landing. The Jackson Pollock-style solution of a cornered eating-disorder suffered to supervised refeeding: splatter rather than swallow the killer calories.

'Eight, nine...' I would be losing my concentration. What did it matter how many steps there were? Sooner or later, I would reach the top. Which I did. And there I confronted the Shake Routine. This involved an interrogation from the whining parasite in Riche's head. You only used soymilk, powder and strawberries? Was it no-fat soymilk, the one in the red carton? Promise you didn't add honey? And you didn't go near meat in the supermarket, did you?

Yes, yes, I promise, no. The lies slipped, as if oiled, from my tongue. *Hail Mary, full of grace…although when I look at my son, I know you're down for the count or afflicted with deafness.*

Finally, Riche would start to drink and even then the course of the ritual was punctuated by the same call and response—insistent questions, resigned answers—and also by frequent tipping of the cup. Variety came in the form of Riche's random attempts to lob the cup and contents down the milk-stained staircase and sometimes, thankfully, a furry Layanese body rubbing itself against my legs. After the shake came teeth-cleaning, spitting, demands to stop spitting, and more spitting.

Tucked within the framework of these five shakes were daily visits—usually in the morning—to Footprints. Four times a week, Riche met with Sonia, once a week with the dietician. This meant that five times a week, I absconded to Mary Ryan's for an hour-long coffee over a magazine. In the near future I would pretend to be someone else at patchwork classes once a week. Afternoons, after the last shake, we visited Games Workshop. Then there was time for a short walk in the fading light in the botanical gardens or the Roma Street Parklands before we returned to the townhouse for Riche's fruit plate. And my chardonnay. Visits to Dr C had been reduced to once a fortnight. In the week off, I slotted in the recently added fortnightly visit to the psychiatrist. Blood tests had been deemed no longer necessary. Tai Chi had bitten the dust.

The other element of our ritual was the daily hunt for strawberries. Sometimes I bought them on my way back to Footprints from Mary Ryan's. If I forgot, I would have to buy them on the way home from Games Workshop or the Roma Street Parklands. There was no way around it. They were an essential ingredient of both the shakes and the evening fruit plate. I would steel myself for the familiar cautions that always followed the news that I needed to make a stop: don't buy bad food, don't go near other food, don't let the strawberries touch other food.

I would park outside the Milton supermarket and, leaving Riche in the car, make my way through the shadows. Inside the store, I shielded my eyes from the fluorescent glare as I wandered through a psychedelic display of acid-yellow lemons, boldly coloured oranges, plump mandarins, and boxes and boxes of apples—Pink Lady, Red Delicious, Sundowner and Fuji. I would resist the urge to buy some of those boxed apples, polished and shiny, lined up like flush-faced cherubs. I couldn't buy apples and strawberries at the same time. That was the rule. I knew I would have to break down this prohibition one day, but there were so many battlefronts, and I was a solitary foot soldier.

So I would walk past the apples and the oranges, the lemons and the mandarins, the pears and the plums, the potatoes, tomatoes, aubergines, rhubarb, carrots and cabbage, by which time I would be reeling with the smell of all this forbidden food. Sometimes I would reach the end of the aisle without finding strawberries. Often I would try two or three shops without success. Once I finally settled for a punnet I found in the refrigerator on the back wall of a Chinese delicatessen on Milton Road. It was the fifth store I'd tried. The strawberries were tiny and discoloured and I saw a faint fuzz of mould on several, but I knew they would have to do. Anorexia pays no heed to seasons. And I needed those strawberries for the fruit plate and the protein shakes that I would have to prepare that night for the next morning.

Riche had gradually reeled in the time of his first protein shake so by late February we were starting at 4 am. I already knew that this demand, apparently common among sufferers, was to allow time to burn off calories, yet I couldn't summon the energy to resist. The dietician had told me to spread the shakes evenly through the day but Riche's inability to drink them anywhere but the apartment meant I had to juggle the times, serving a shake half an hour early here, half an hour late there. The last two shakes of the day ended up roughly two hours apart, the final one at 4.30 pm so we could go to Games Workshop—a survival decision. I served the fruit plate at around 8 pm, later on Friday nights because of the Games Workshop gaming session. Each night I delivered the plate to his room. Not knowing any better, I would leave Riche with a limp stricture—*you must eat it all*—to supervise his meal, if a plate of fruit can be thus defined.

Or perhaps I left him because it was 8 pm or later and I'd been up since 4 am even though I thought I'd finished with early morning feeds eleven years ago and I wanted a glass or two of chardonnay (who was I kidding; I wanted three or four) and the thought of watching him dissect his apple as if it were a dead rat in a laboratory made me want to throw up or scream or bang my head against the wall just as he did when the voice in his head grew too loud.

When I returned to his room I would find picked-off pieces of apple assembled into a small shrine on his plate.

○

Week in, week out, the same old visits, the same old walks, the same old fruit plate and the same old drudgery, up and down the infernal staircase with the shakes, Riche's elixir of life.

I couldn't tell you the total number of stairs: I never did count them all. I *can* tell you that I went down at various paces. If I had just given Riche the last protein shake of the day, I took the steps at a moderate clip. If Riche had allowed the milky fluid to pool in the sides of his cheeks so he could later spit it out, if he had spat and coughed repeatedly while he cleaned his teeth so that I feared he would vomit, then I trudged slowly down the stairs. Occasionally, to escape the parasite's voice, I took the steps too fast and tripped.

But on a good day—a day when the parasite seemed quieter, a single run through the questions sufficed and spitting and coughing were easy to control—I held the empty cup in my hand like a trophy on my way down, and took the steps two at a time.

When the alarm rang I hauled myself out of bed. If circumstances were different and Kevin was living with us, he and I together might have marshalled the strength to put our combined feet down at this ungodly hour of starting. As it was, I was working with a theory often applied to two-year-olds: pick your battles, and the most important battle was that the shakes should be drunk at all, so I pulled on my robe and walked across the landing to Riche's room.

He was sleeping on his side, his legs drawn up, dressed in his grey trousers and a T-shirt with the words *read the signs* scrawled across the chest. Below were nine circles. One contained the peace symbol, the others slogans: *say no to drugs*, *don't waste water* (which seemed downright tasteless under the circumstances), *help the homeless*, *stop pollution*, *save the planet*, *recycle*, *end racism*, and finally—the only slogan that should have concerned an almost-twelve-year-old—*go to school*. The shirt had seemed cute when I'd bought it a year ago for my environmental warrior.

'Wake up Riche,' I said. 'Time for your shake.'

Riche opened his eyes, and I saw childish innocence in them for an instant. Then full consciousness claimed him, and they became the eyes of someone who knew things a child had no business knowing.

'You awake?'

Riche nodded. I left him to wash his hands and went downstairs to wash *my* hands, fetch the shake and carry it, and the heavy weight of anxiety that chewed at my stomach, upstairs to my son. The basic shape of the routine remained the same, but each component was worsening: handwashing that threatened to scour the skin from his bones, questions looping continuously, repeated tipping of the cup that aimed to spread the viscous fluid up the sides, teeth-cleaning that would surely wear away the enamel and, worst of all, hawking and spitting that stopped just short of vomiting.

The gruelling ordeal over, I returned to bed and slipped into a troubled dream, from which I was wrenched awake by a crashing from Riche's bathroom.

The toilet seat. It had slammed down onto the pedestal—he must have lowered it with his feet again, just as he had a few days before. It made sense. The smooth plastic was an ideal surface for the accumulation of germs. I wanted to go down to the kitchen to make coffee but waited. Riche's bathroom door would be open because he couldn't touch doorknobs, and I didn't want to disturb his privacy.

The next shake was no easier. By the time it was finished, I decided I was ready to say 'yes' to drugs; I would have Riche's antidepressant prescription filled. A few millilitres of Prozac surely couldn't mess his brain up any more than starvation. We could make it a mother–son activity: 'Time for our antidepressants, darling.'

I had started taking Zoloft soon after my mother's stroke. She and I had always had a fraught relationship—a violent collision of generational differences not helped, I suspected, by her undiagnosed underlying depression. Mine too, quite possibly. When she emerged brain-damaged from a coma, and I knew I had lost forever the chance to repair our relationship, I found myself having obsessive black thoughts, doubting my ability to mother my children. The Zoloft had helped me. If I started Riche on Prozac it might make his life, and mine, bearable.

At nine o'clock, I told Riche I was going to the shops. 'I need to buy more water for you,' I said.

'Don't get it near any food.'

At the shopping centre, I dug around in my bag, which was a jumble of tissues, shopping receipts, loose coins, Steven Levenkron's *Anatomy of Anorexia* and an assortment of pens, until I found the torn and grubby Prozac prescription. I handed it over to the pharmacist. After a second's thought, I also handed over the script for the anti-psychotic. To be on the safe side.

'Has your son had these before?'

'No. He has anorexia. The psychiatrist thinks the Prozac might help with his obsessive symptoms…' I stopped. The pharmacist's look of mild alarm, as if I'd stepped too close, told me that once again I'd said more than necessary. 'The other one's just for emergencies.'

The pharmacist showed me the bottle of Prozac. 'Start with half a spoonful at the same time each day.'

I nodded. 'We're good at schedules.'

'Alcohol consumption should be kept to a minimum.' He paused. 'I don't suppose that's an issue here.'

'No.' I said. At any rate, not with my son.

After paying for the Prozac and the Zyprexa, I bought six bottles of The Original Adam's Ale Pure Australian Water—my alibi—in case Riche was at his post on the staircase when I arrived home. After I'd put the water away, I took the Prozac upstairs, anxiety again eating away at my insides, the muscles across my shoulders turning to boards.

'I'm going to start you on antidepressant medication,' I used what I regarded as my no-nonsense voice. 'Dr S says it will make you feel less anxious.'

'I'm not taking it,' Riche said. He backed towards the wall but stopped a few centimetres short, as if he had run into a silent alarm system that warned him off the contaminated surface. 'It'll make me fat. You can't make me have it.'

For the next fifty minutes, I tried to convince Riche that the drug wouldn't make him fat. At last, he agreed to take it. It seemed to be my persistence rather than my logic that worked: the look on his face was of resignation. I half-filled the transparent plastic spoon with the clear liquid and held it out.

'Here, take it.'

Riche shook his head. Cornered-animal eyes. 'I don't want to touch the spoon,' he said.

Pick your battles. 'Okay. Open your mouth.'

Riche tipped his head back and opened his mouth. I emptied the liquid onto his tongue and told him to swallow. His Adam's apple bobbed up and down.

'Open your mouth.'

Riche opened his mouth: the medicine was gone. The rawness in my stomach eased; my shoulder muscles relaxed. I'd done it! But my relief was short lived. His next protein shake was due. I put the medicine away, washed my hands and fetched a shake and then we swung into another round of exhausting questions and answers.

'You only used soymilk, powder and strawberries?'

'Yes.' My voice as robotic and mono-tonal as his ever was.

'Was it no-fat soymilk, the one in the red carton?'

'Yes.'

'Promise you didn't add honey?'

'No, I didn't add honey.'

'And you didn't go near meat in the supermarket, did you?'

'No, I didn't go near meat in the supermarket.'

Several times over. Our endlessly discordant duet, interspersed with foot-scraping and shuffling, cup-tipping and shaking, and mini-crises when he held the darned thing aloft and threatened to pitch it at the wall.

○

The day was not going to improve: we had an appointment with a paediatrician, the last item on my shopping list for exile. The dietician had reluctantly told me that Riche's weight had increased by three kilograms in total—not enough by a long shot, but surely enough to convince a paediatrician that Riche was safe at home. Riche, naturally, was not keen. To make matters worse, I had scheduled the appointment for noon, and Riche's next shake that day was due at 1 pm.

The territory was familiar. Dr Holt's office was at the Wesley Hospital, where we went for the blood tests with Trish. We made our way up in the elevator without incident, but ran into trouble in the reception area of Dr Holt's office when a young boy carrying french fries walked in with his heavily pregnant mother. Riche saw the fries and bolted out, down the corridor towards the elevator. I raced after him. The elevator door started to open just as I neared it. Arms outstretched, I lunged in front of Riche so as to block his way.

'*No!*' Did I shout? 'Don't even think about it.'

A man stepped out and gave us a suspicious look as he walked off. *Stay away from Madwoman and Ghost-boy.* The elevator door closed and I lowered my arms.

'You have to come back to see the doctor,' I said. 'This is one of those no-choice deals.'

'The boy had bad food.'

'It won't hurt you.'

'I'll get fat.'

'Calories can't fly through air.'

Same lines, different day. Over and over and over, until finally Riche yielded to my implacable stance. Even then, he refused to enter the reception area, instead lingering in the corridor, by the door. I explained the situation to the receptionist.

'Don't worry,' she said. 'He can come in when it's his turn.'

I thanked her and took the seat nearest the door. The receptionist told the mother of the little boy that the doctor was ready to see them, and they disappeared through a door on the far side of the reception area. Still Riche refused to come in. A short time later, a woman appeared in the door through which the mother and her boy had gone and called Riche's name.

'Come on,' I said to my son.

He didn't move.

I looked at the receptionist. 'He's afraid that the french fries are in Dr Holt's office.'

The receptionist reassured Riche that the boy and his mother had gone in to see the obstetrician in the same suite of offices. Riche still looked worried, but he came in and we followed Dr Holt.

Dressed in a slim-fitting skirt and a cream blouse, she extended a neatly manicured hand which I took, hoping she wouldn't notice my bitten-down fingernails.

'Will you both have a seat?'

I explained why Riche needed to stand, took a seat in front of the desk and inspected the photos, grouped to one side, of Dr Holt with young twins.

I answered the familiar questions, and Riche put up the familiar resistance when the doctor tried to examine him. He reluctantly agreed to her measuring his pulse after she had performed the handwashing ritual. But when Dr Holt picked up her stethoscope, he backed away.

'It won't hurt you,' I droned, my response automatic. We would run through this tiresome performance a few times and then it would be over. 'It's all right, it won't make you fat.'

'*Fuck you!*' Riche screamed. His eyes burned with fury and he kicked out at my shins.

Dr Holt took a step back. I gaped at my son. He was swearing at me? He never ever swore at me. I leaned forward, bending from the waist so his feet couldn't reach my shins. 'That's the anorexia speaking, not you.' Useless words, and I knew it. I turned to Dr Holt. 'Could you wipe your stethoscope so Riche knows it's clean?'

'Sure.' Dr Holt dampened a paper towel and rubbed the diaphragm of the stethoscope.

'Come on Riche,' I said. 'It's clean.'

'Fuck you,' Riche repeated, his voice loud and sharp with anger, as if I had suggested he allow the doctor to brand him with a hot iron. He aimed a few more kicks at my shins. The effort seemed to tire him, and the ferocity of the kicks diminished. Finally he stopped and stood panting while Dr Holt listened to his heart and wrapped the cuff around his left arm to check his blood pressure.

'That'll do,' she said. 'I think this is stressing Riche too much. His blood pressure is low, but his hydration is good and the blood test and ECG results Dr C sent along are good, so I'm happy for him to stay out of hospital. Come and see me again if you're worried, otherwise Dr C can continue monitoring Riche. I don't think it's a good idea for him to see too many doctors.'

I thanked the doctor, and thanked god for the doctor, and paid the bill. This was a victory. The paediatrician had confirmed that I had successfully rehydrated Riche at home, despite the first psychiatrist's insistence that Riche would need urgent hospitalisation to reach this point. But I had no time to appreciate the significance of the moment because Riche rallied as soon as we were in the car, a defiant set to his face.

'I'm not having the next shake,' he said.

'Don't worry.' I spat the words at my son. To date I'd done a pretty good job of separating the boy from the anorexic behaviour but I was only human. 'I'm not putting myself through it after that performance.' For once, we'd miss one.

The grey skies seemed to press down and a restless wind idled in the trees as I turned the car down Milton Road, heading towards Footprints of Angels. I needed to talk about this to someone who would understand.

Riche looked confused. 'Where are we going?'

'Don't say a word,' I said. 'Not one. I've had about enough.'

He sank back into his seat.

I parked the car alongside the tall brushwood fence of the clinic. 'Stay right where you are,' I said. 'Don't move a muscle.'

I got out of the car and slammed the door. Without so much as a backward glance, I unlatched the gate and let myself into the garden, fairly sure that Riche would be too afraid of contamination to open the car door himself. Upstairs, I asked for Sonia.

'She's not here,' another therapist said.

I burst into tears and told her what had happened. 'Riche was awful,' I sobbed. 'I can't do this anymore.'

The woman gave me a tissue, sat me down, made me a cup of tea and agreed that yes, the illness was horrible. She listened some more. I drank the tea. And then it was time to go home.

○

I described the scene in the paediatrician's office at my next appointment with Dr C.

'I hope she doesn't think Riche's always like that.' There was a pause while I waited for Dr C to reassure me.

'Why don't you write to her and tell her what he's really like?' she said.

And that was a rib breaker. I'd expected to be told that people saw beyond Riche's illness-behaviour to the real Riche. The boy who, until the last few months, brought home a trail of school reports that said, 'Intelligent, self-motivated, positive and perceptive, Riche is a joy to teach,' 'Riche has, as always, been a model student this year,' 'Riche is an enthusiastic and co-operative class member.' Every report he had ever received made similar comments. The boy who at age six made people weep when he thanked me in an impromptu speech at my birthday party for being a great mother. I remembered this boy;

I saw glimpses of him still. I saw it when he turned to me in the car one day and asked, his voice soft, if I thought he was trying with the shakes. As if he yearned for me to know that he didn't mean to make my life difficult. But apparently this was not the boy other people saw. Not even Dr C.

The front door clicked shut behind me as my visitors left, once more sealing our townhouse from the outside world. Crumbs littered the kitchen bench ('We brought an iced bun for morning tea. Is that all right?') but I headed straight for the stairs. I thought I'd better check on Riche before cleaning up. At the top of the stairs something caught my eye. A splash of red on the beige tiles of his bathroom floor. Blood? I went over to the door. Angry red streaks slashed my reflection in the mirror. The basin was also spattered with blood. A wave of dizziness hit me, my legs threatened to give way and my pulse hammered in my ears. I leaned against the doorjamb and called out.

Riche appeared at his bedroom door. He held his bloodied arms away from his sides, his fingers splayed.

I tasted bile in the back of my throat. 'What have you done to yourself?'

Riche looked down, said nothing. He was twitching and jerking like a marionette in the grasp of a toddler.

'Show me your hands.'

He held them out, palms down. They were covered with congealed blood.

Had he slashed his wrists? I swallowed hard. 'Turn them over.'

He turned his palms up; they too were covered in blood, but although the skin over his wrists was bloodied it had not been cut.

'What did you do?'

'They brought that bun.' Riche stared through me, eyes unfocused. His voice had a mechanical quality, as if it were programmed. 'It was covered in bad things. It's going to make me fat.' He looked down at his arms and his eyes grew large with horror. 'I'm getting fatter already.'

'It was just a bun,' I said. I let go of the doorjamb and stepped towards him.

'It was bad.' He continued in his strange, flat tone. 'I saw it. You told me they wouldn't bring bad food.'

'For crying out loud, it was just a bun.'

'I wanted to clean my hands. I didn't want it to make me fat.'

'You did that from scrubbing?' I pointed at his hands, all the time feeling that nothing, not even the concrete floor beneath me, could save me from falling.

'It wasn't enough. I had to use my nails,' he said. 'I'm fat.'

I shook my head. 'I'll find some bandages.'

I hurried to my bedroom only to be stopped short by the sight of bloody spots—indecipherable graffiti—on one of my bedroom walls. Riche must have flicked it from his hands. 'What the *fuck* is this?'

Riche materialised in my door. 'You let them in.' He sounded accusing now.

Jo and Annemarie, friends from Mullumbimby, my first visitors other than Kevin and the children in the couple of months since we'd moved to Brisbane. No phone calls either, except for one close friend and a cousin from Perth. I made tea and we sat on stools at the bench, me on the kitchen side. From there I could keep an eye on those architecturally elegant spy holes Riche made such good use of. After forty-five minutes we'd run out of things to say. We hugged and kissed and they made generous promises to visit again. I knew they wouldn't and I understood: Riche's illness had become a monomania

179

for me, and monomania of any kind is difficult to be near.

Now I sank to my bed and put my head in my hands. *He can't help it. He's sick. Don't yell at him.* I looked up and took a few deep breaths. Riche looked penitent.

'Let me wash your hands.' I ran the tap in my bathroom. 'Here, put them under the water.'

Riche allowed the stream of water to wash over his hands and tolerated, grudgingly, my touch. I wiped the blood away.

'I'll put some cream on your hands.' *Stupid*, I thought instantly as Riche raised his hands, shield-like, and recoiled. I should have said 'lotion' or 'ointment' or 'balm'. Or I could have bamboozled Riche's anorexia with 'antipruritic'. I had a thesaurus of words to choose from, and I had latched onto the one that sounded fattening.

'All right, I won't,' I said. 'It wouldn't make you fat, but I know your anorexia is telling you it would.'

I bandaged his hands, careful to use dressings and bandages with sealed wrappings so Riche would know they weren't contaminated. And then, after wiping the walls and sponging the carpet, I took Riche into Games Workshop: distraction for him and respite for me.

In this world of geeks, Riche looked less out of place. No one here knew about his illness or if they did, they didn't comment on it. The staff members seemed genuinely fond of Riche. They responded to his bright-eyed enthusiasm and treated him like a mascot. Riche, in turn, thrived on the overtly masculine energy. His arrival sparked the usual greetings.

'Hey champ,' one staff member called.

'Riche, mate,' from another. 'What's up with your hands?'

Riche bowed his head and dismissed their questions with a shrug and then sidled up to the gaming table, where a group of boys had their troops on the offensive. A debate was raging over who got to move what where. Riche cleared his throat and half a dozen expectant faces turned towards him. He had put the long solitary hours in his darkened room to good use: he was known at Games Workshop as the Walking Rulebook. Even the staff deferred to his judgment in a contested ruling. Now everyone waited for him to hand down his decision, which he did in an authoritative manner before the battle proceeded.

Satisfied that the morning's crisis was over, I set off on my usual run to Borders in search of some new books for Riche and any additions I could find for my eating-disorder library. The anorexia books shared a shelf with sex guides, and who, I wondered, had devised that strange coupling? I made a selection. Was it Kathryn Zerbe's *The Body Betrayed* that day? Or another of the fifteen or so eating-disorder books I bought in just under two months, a frantic accumulation, the lines from one book blurring into the next, a seemingly endless stream of recrimination. For any of them the date of purchase was soon forgotten. But lines such as Zerbe's comment on the mother–child bond—'For an eating disorder to develop, some aspect or aspects of the relationship must have gone awry'—burned themselves into my consciousness.

Downstairs the woman behind the coffee-shop counter smiled at me. 'The usual?'

My routine order of raisin toast and a cappuccino was both a comfort and a small embarrassment, since I suspected it looked like an eccentric rebuke to the bewildering array of food on display at the counter. But the truth was, my appetite had evaporated and I was eating for nutrition, not pleasure. Sometimes not even nutrition, so fraught had the issue of food become. I just didn't want to have to make choices.

In any case, after a few mouthfuls I pushed the plate away and drank my coffee. When that was finished I sucked a mint to sanitise my breath before I collected Riche and took him to the townhouse, a place I steadfastly refused to call home.

'You didn't have a coffee or go near McDonald's did you?' he said, when I gave him his books.

'No,' I said. *As if!*

Kevin sounded cheerful during our nightly conjugal conversation.

'Did you remember to vote?' he said.

Damn, it was March 22nd. I should have registered my postal vote in the state election. Not that I really cared. As far as I knew, neither the Liberal Party nor the Labor Party offered an improved deal for anorexia treatment. As for the Greens, they would have to save the planet without me.

'Don't worry. I'll visit you in jail.' There it was again: the involuntary chuckle in his voice that never failed to rile me.

'You think that's funny?'

Our marriage was falling apart and he made a joke? And what would happen to Riche if I were jailed? Did he think about that? And did he consider my feelings when he joked while I was lumped with the task of looking after Riche when the whole damn thing was his fault? The freight train was rolling, fuelled as always by the black coal of my anger.

Finally I ran out of steam. Not even the sound of Kevin's breath broke the electronic silence.

'Jeez,' he said at last. 'What do you mean our marriage is falling apart? I thought we were getting on okay, considering. We're both just stressed because Riche's sick.'

I cringe now. When I think back to that tirade, a rant worthy of any glassy-eyed fanatic, I'm amazed by Kevin's response, too. The restraint in his silence; the grace he showed even as another volley of blame hurtled in his direction, when all he'd wanted was to make me smile. But still I would cut myself some slack, unhinged as I was by the unexpected ramifications of eating an iced bun.

○

My temper had cooled by the time Kevin rang the following evening. I told him that Riche and I had spent most of the day in the townhouse that still wasn't home, apart from a visit to Games Workshop and a brisk march in the botanical gardens.

'Sounds like Riche's happier,' Kevin said. 'I think you made the right decision with that townhouse.'

'Thanks.' I felt the distance between us contract just a little. It had been a while since either of us had admitted to being wrong about anything. 'Riche likes having a separate room to make his models, but he needs a table or desk.'

'I could organise a desk.' Kevin sounded eager. 'I'll do it this weekend when I come up.'

'Great,' I said. 'Just let me ask him first.'

Riche had cloistered himself in his room during the family's previous visit to the townhouse, but had otherwise handled the invasion reasonably well. Now, when I told him of Kevin's offer, he agreed but listed his conditions: Kevin had to wash his hands, he wasn't allowed to eat or drink while he bought the desk, and he couldn't buy the desk from a shop near McDonald's. I said that went without saying: Dad knew the rules. Riche grunted. He would accept the desk.

I'm sitting at a different desk, years later. It stands in a small corner room of a house in the Blue Mountains, west of Sydney. An open window admits the fresh mountain air, scented by towering Norfolk pines, along with the angry voices of a couple in a neighbouring house. And perhaps it's the sound of those raised voices that makes me linger on Riche's grunt and what it said and didn't say in the context of his ongoing and silent fight with his father. At the time, I felt only a frisson of excitement that he'd responded at all, as if a door had been cracked open to a previously forbidden room. Now I find myself wishing that I could rewrite that scene and find words for the mother that would encourage her son to say 'yes'. To accept his father, instead of merely a desk. Because surely that grunt left much yearning unsaid. The retrospectoscope, I'm beginning to understand, is an instrument to be handled with care. It concentrates memories in much the same way that a lens concentrates the sun's rays; and they too have the power to burn.

○

I was propping up the kitchen bench as usual when two smiling faces appeared at the sliding glass doors behind the kitchen. Once inside, the children tiptoed around the living area, opening cupboard doors, most of which they quickly shut when they noticed the persistent theme of the books inside. Louise stroked the carpet on the scratching post. 'Where are the kittens?' She spoke in a hushed tone.

'Upstairs.'

Louise looked longingly up the staircase, but I smiled and shook my head. A few seconds later a kitten shot out from the stairway and onto the scratching post, where it clawed furiously. Louise laughed, picked the kitten up and with a broad smile, buried her face in its fur.

Riche's protein shake was due, his first with the rest of the family present in the townhouse. He added a few extra questions about whether anyone else had been near the shake, but eventually took the cup from me and drank. With that small victory in hand, I took him to Games Workshop while Kevin took Andy and Louise desk shopping.

Riche and I returned to the townhouse in time for his next shake. I was rinsing the empty cup in the kitchen sink when the rest of the family appeared. Kevin carried a flat cardboard package in and balanced it near the staircase.

'Where should I make it up?'

'In Riche's painting room, away from the kitchen,' I said. 'Hang on a minute. I need to warn him.'

But first a cuddle for Louise. I felt a pang under the ribs as I settled her on the sofa with her toys. Two Barbies and a sea of tiny outfits.

'Want to help me dress Barbie?' she said.

'I can't, sweetheart.'

'Then can I watch a video?'

'Sure,' I said. What was one more on top of the dozens she'd watched in recent weeks? 'Get Dad to put it on.'

Upstairs, I found Riche pacing his room, a book in his hands.

'Sit down,' I said. 'You know you're not to walk while you read.' I folded my arms across my chest and assumed what I hoped was an attitude that meant business. Riche sat down and started to jiggle his legs. The rapid rhythmic movement frayed the edges of my nerves. 'Dad's bought the desk. I think he should assemble it in your painting room, so you know it didn't get near food.'

'He won't try and talk to me, will he?' The jiggling sped up.

'He won't say a word.'

Riche stood and resumed his pacing, still holding his open book. 'He'll have clean hands, won't he? And he has to go downstairs when he's finished. I don't want him thinking he can come up here whenever he wants.'

I reassured him, told him to sit down again and went down to help Kevin with the package. As we passed Riche's door I could see him sitting on his bed, the fragile curve of his back towards us. He probably weighed less than the box Kevin and I were carrying. Was it possible he wanted more than anything to throw himself into his father's arms but didn't know how to bridge the gap? I was afraid to ask.

Kevin hated handyman jobs and preferred, where possible, to pay someone to do it for him. That he was doing this for Riche showed me how deeply he regretted the fracture in their relationship. It was almost as if he sought to reach his son through the grain of the desk. I wished him luck and left, closing the door behind me.

When I went back an hour later, wood and screws were strewn over the floor and a pile of torn cardboard and plastic lay in the corner. Kevin was trying to join two pieces of the desk.

'Fuck it, this is impossible. Can you hold these steady for me?'

I held the pieces of wood while Kevin screwed them together. Then he picked up the instruction sheet and pointed to a particular numbered screw.

'I can't find this one anywhere. Can you take a look?'

I rummaged around in the pile of screws and found the one Kevin was missing and then I left him to it.

It took another hour and much more cursing, until at last a serviceable-looking desk stood in the middle of the room. Kevin ran his hand over the brown wood. 'I hope he likes it.'

He did. Each day, he spent hours at the desk, always standing, as he glued the pieces of his tiny warriors together and painted them— sometimes four or five different colours on a model no more than two centimetres tall. As to what he was thinking when it came to his father, I couldn't even begin to imagine. There was certainly no outward change in his attitude towards Kevin. In fact, he started talking about changing his last name by deed poll. It was as if he wanted to remove all trace of Kevin and his grandmother from his life. He said he preferred my maiden name. And in a personal anti-war statement, he wanted to lose the association with his country of birth that rode on his middle name, Samuel. That saddened me. Riche had always loved being an American citizen. As a small child he had claimed to have a different accent from us. 'I say tom-ay-toe, and you say tom-ar-toe, Mummy,' he would say, but anorexia had made him obsessively anti-war and anti-American. His new middle name, he announced, would be Henry.

The face that stared from my bathroom mirror in the grey dawn light of an April morning could have been my seventy-six-year-old mother's. The bags below my eyes, which I had inherited as a physical characteristic from her, had swollen, making me look like an ancient shar pei. I ran the pads of my middle fingers over the doughy skin, smoothing it out. Twenty years previously, when I was working as a doctor in the emergency department of the Alfred Hospital in Sydney, I had undergone plastic surgery to get rid of those bags.

They were back within fifteen years, by which time I had seen a few too many photos of celebrities who had been sucked into the plastic surgery cycle. Now, twenty years after surgery, they were worse than ever. Stress, I thought. Stress is taking years off my life. I released the skin and watched the shar pei slump back into position. I didn't stop to wonder if there were similarities between my preoccupations and Riche's fear of fat. It was 4 am, and Riche needed his first shake for the day.

○

By eleven o'clock, Riche had finished that and two more shakes. It was a Saturday and Kevin wasn't arriving with Louise and Andy until late afternoon, so I dropped Riche at Games Workshop and wandered down to Myers. A few ornaments would be nice, to display in the shelves that framed the back door of our bleak little townhouse. I chose a ceramic elephant. It reminded me of a piece Riche had written for home schooling the previous year, an assignment that asked for a description of an imaginary elephant statue, supposedly stolen during a break-in. Eleven-year-old Riche wrote:

I am looking for my Indian Hindu elephant statue. My statue shines and has magnificent white tusks. My elephant has raised its trunk to trumpet. It has a saddle with eight red tassels. If you find my elephant you will know it is mine by the way its Asian eyes, perfectly oval, stare at you eternally.

The Myers elephant lacked a red tasselled saddle but, like Riche's elephant, it raised its trunk as if to trumpet. A gesture, it seemed to me, of defiance and hope.

It was on my way back to Games Workshop that I started to feel faint. Spots and wavy lines shimmered and danced in the periphery of my vision. This had happened to me at least half a dozen times in the last two years and I had always assumed it indicated an underlying but not serious metabolic problem. Whatever the cause, I knew what it meant: I needed calories, and fast. I hurried to the juice stand in the mall and ordered an apple and pineapple juice. Cup in hand, I shuffled to a bench and, as I sipped the cool tart liquid, I imagined the sugar molecules slipping into my bloodstream and bobbing along like sailboats on the red tide to my brain. Past episodes had taught me it would take a few minutes for my vision to clear completely. If I moved, the symptoms would worsen. But a glance at my watch showed that it was almost closing time for Myers, and Riche and I needed to walk through Myers to reach the elevator bank that took us down to the underground carpark. The alternative route involved the food shops in the arcade, and that would be difficult. I gathered my shopping and stood up, but a wave of dizziness forced me back down.

I called out to two policemen, explained my problem and asked if they would possibly be able to fetch Riche. The policemen looked dubiously at each other but went off in search of my son. I rested against the seatback. The mall was crowded with shoppers enjoying the early autumn sunshine. A teenage girl wearing a midriff shirt and low-slung jeans walked past with a tub of french fries. A creamy apron of flesh wobbled with every step she took. I wouldn't be caught dead, I thought. I closed my eyes and waited for my vision to clear.

When I was that girl's age I had just left school, and with it a uniform that included a tie and a stiff, wide-brimmed straw hat. Eager to make the most of my new-found sartorial independence, I wanted to buy my first pair of jeans, so I went with one of my medical school friends to Jeans West and tried some on. But when I strutted in front of the full-length mirror in a pair of size six hipsters, I saw that my thighs made a slight bulge against the denim instead of the smooth line I wanted. My beanpole girlfriend left the store in her new 501s. I left empty-handed.

Strange that I could believe I was too fat for jeans when I knew, at some level, I had always been thinner than most of my peers. My father-in-law said of me later, 'You can't fatten a thoroughbred.' Which may be true of racehorses, but I never ate enough to put it to the test. I made an egg and Vegemite sandwich for breakfast and a banana sandwich for dinner. Lunch was a cheese sandwich or sticky bun from the hospital cafeteria. Between meals I stuck to coffee and cigarettes. Late at night, when I had finally shut my Robbins *Basic Pathology*, I half-filled an empty Vegemite jar with Kahlua and drank while I wrote letters that I never sent to boys who didn't seem to know I existed.

I ate enough to get through the day, but no more. And that was fine. I also exercised. In fact, I skipped morning lectures to ride my bicycle ten kilometres to the local swimming pool. This seemed perfectly reasonable behaviour to me. I churned up and down a lane for an hour or so in a one-piece swimming suit. A bikini was not an option for a girl who was too fat for jeans.

When I opened my eyes again, the girl with the hot chips and the generous midriff had disappeared. But as I sat in the mall and waited for Riche, I wondered what had crossed her mind when she dressed that morning. Perhaps where I saw fat she saw Rubenesque curves? Was it possible that she simply didn't care? I would no sooner parade even a sliver of wobbling flesh than walk naked down the mall. We might as well have been females of different species. Still, I envied whatever it was that allowed her to brazenly expose flesh I would not have allowed to accumulate in the first place. And somewhere, at the limits of my conscious thought, hovered a huge question mark over an unspoken and incompletely formed suspicion.

The shimmering lines in my field of vision were annoying. I worried that, left unchecked, they would progress to loss of consciousness. And what, really, had caused them? The need to know seemed more urgent than it once had. Riche depended on me; I couldn't afford to black out. I closed my eyes again and kept still. I remembered a doctor I'd seen two years previously, when the symptoms had first appeared. He looked at me and asked me to climb onto the scales. Forty-eight kilograms, at 5 feet and 7 inches tall. That gave me a body mass index of 16.6, significantly below the normal range of 18.5–24.9.

When the doctor asked me if I had anorexia I was horrified. Now, in the light of Riche's illness, I grasped at that elusive suspicion and, for the first time ever, considered the possibility that my food intake was low compared with other women I knew and that perhaps this, along with too much coffee and a low bodyweight, caused low blood sugar levels, which in turn produced the strange visual effects. After all, food certainly reversed the symptoms. Maybe my eating had been disordered for a very long time. A mother and a son: nature or nurture?

Saturday afternoon shopping sounds penetrated my cocoon: children squealing, a one-sided conversation on a cell phone, a Delta

Goodrem song from a nearby store. And, finally, Riche's voice, strained and anxious. When I opened my eyes and saw the look on his face, I knew I needed to attend to my own health as well as his.

○

Later that afternoon, I heard the front gate of our townhouse clang and Louise burst in through the door with a painting to show me. 'Red valour, carmine courageous…' She chanted the fantastical names of colours she had learned at her Steiner school.

Andy fished around in his daypack and whipped out a piece of cloth. He shook it and held it up for inspection.

'Jacqui and I made it,' he said. 'It's a chiton, like they wore in ancient Greece.'

I admired Andy's handiwork and worried, not for the first time, about his education. Jacqui did her best under difficult circumstances. She set maths exercises and read Greek myths with him, and together they had produced some stunning art projects. But she had her hands full and home schooling wasn't really her brief. Sooner or later he probably needed to go to school. But not yet. I didn't want to force him to start somewhere new when I wasn't there to help him adjust. He had enough to manage with his brother's illness, and the separation from me.

Kevin came in at last and we settled the children in front of a video and took two glasses of wine out to the rear courtyard As we sipped our chardonnay, I told him what had happened in the mall.

'I'm pretty sure I'm not anorexic,' I said, 'but I might have some kind of sub-threshold eating disorder.'

'What the hell does that mean?'

'Well, I guess I'm too thin, and I don't particularly like the idea of putting on weight. But I still get my period.'

'You know, ever since I've known you, you've had this thing about food. You've always talked about having a fast metabolism and how much you eat. And for years I've believed you, I've gone around saying, "My wife's always eating. She eats more than I do." But it's bullshit. You serve me a ton of food and I eat the lot and get fat while you push the food around your plate, and then you're starving and feeling faint an hour later when we've gone out, and there's this panic to find food.'

Kevin was right. I only ever ate small amounts. Food just didn't interest me the way it seemed to interest him. It was a necessity, not a recreation, and when he lingered over choosing an ice cream or a pizza, I wanted to shout with frustration.

Kevin brought his chair closer, draped an arm around my shoulders and pulled me towards him at an awkward angle. I tugged at his arm. 'Watch it, you're hurting my back.' Christ, maybe years of undereating had given me osteoporosis as well. I would end up looking like Quasimodo.

He relaxed his hold but left his arm there, and I allowed myself to find comfort in its weight.

'I liked the way you looked though. I never thought you were too skinny.'

True, Kevin preferred the waif look. Kate Moss rather than Claudia Schiffer.

'You didn't cause my food issues,' I said. He hadn't encouraged me to eat either, but then why should he? What you eat isn't really a problem—until it's a problem.

'Well, what did then?' Kevin said.

I shrugged. We sat in silence for a few minutes. A warm breeze rustled the leaves of the gum tree behind the courtyard and carried the smell of frying meat from the neighbours' kitchen.

'So what will you do?'

'I'll talk to Jan.' I stood to go indoors. 'Maybe I should have a session with the dietician.'

'Great. Another 120 bucks a week. We're keeping that place afloat.'

I stiffened. 'You just have to be an arsehole, don't you?'

'Come on, honey. I was joking. I think it's a great idea for you to see the dietician. You've got to be strong for Riche.'

The same old dance. But this time, the pleading in Kevin's eyes won me over. I returned his hug and we went inside, taking care to open and close the door quickly to keep the neighbours' barbecue smells at bay.

Fat had long held a negative connotation for me but I didn't know how I had developed the notion of those identical twins: fat-and-greedy and fat-and-lazy. Certainly not from my mother, who was neither greedy nor lazy, but had been overweight since my early childhood. In the heat of Kalgoorlie, where I grew up, she floated around in a tent dress that swung from her body in emerald and turquoise folds. I loved the ocean-deep colours of that dress. But I did wish my mother were slimmer.

I loved my Barbie, too, with her pinched-in waist and smooth hips; I loved the way her thighs retained their sinuous curves when I moved her legs to make her walk. By high school, my passion for Barbie had faded but still she kept watch over me from a display shelf in my bedroom. I knew she would have looked great in jeans.

But hell, thousands of girls played with Barbies without developing eating disorders. And where did all this leave my daughter? She was holding Cinderella Barbie right now as she watched her video. Alongside her, two other Barbies waited for their share of attention. It was crazy, this worry about the effect of well-dressed plastic on my daughter's mental health.

When Kevin, Andy and Louise had gone off to have their dinner, I heated a handful of frozen chips and a frozen piece of crumbed fish in the oven. Then I sat at the counter with my plate in front of me and propped up Susie Orbach's book *Hunger Strike*, which I'd only just got around to reading.

Another dose of maternal dysfunction. When you think about it, mothers are sitting ducks, the obvious if unimaginative target. Orbach said anorectic mothers passed on their own insecurities about their bodies to their daughters. Mealtimes became a power struggle, reflecting the mother's need to be appreciated. For the mother, fat stood for 'need, greed, indulgence, wantonness, unruliness, a loss of control, an unstoppability'.

This wanton unstoppability of mine was apparently society's fault, a verdict that did nothing to ease the guilt that sat, rather more heavily than reheated fish and chips, in the pit of my stomach. Nor did it help me figure out how to manage Riche. As to whether or not I—or Kevin—was a toxic influence in Riche's life, the point was moot. Proving it either way wasn't going to help Riche.

Orbach's analysis was all about mothers and daughters. All the books so far had been. Information on boys with anorexia seemed thin on the ground. Not that the process differed greatly as far as I could see. In fact it was relevant that Riche was younger than most sufferers, although I was years off acquiring even that knowledge. Rachel Bryant-Waugh and Dasha Nicholls write in *Eating Disorders in Children and Adolescents* that 'most childhood presentations of AN are characterised by restriction and exercise rather than associated with bingeing and purging.' More specifically, 'in boys, concern related to fitness and health is often part of the clinical picture… Many boys engage in overexercising, and there is often an association with obsessive-compulsive traits.' That certainly applied to Riche.

But interesting as this information is, knowing it would have made little difference at the time. All I knew was that Riche shared the same distorted vision of his size as the girls and showed the same resistance to treatment. The problem for us was that the clinic, unsurprisingly, wasn't geared for boys. From the name to the décor to the day program activities (not that Riche could participate in the latter), the place screamed 'female'. Day program worked well for the girls; it was a pretty good outpatient support model for sufferers too unwell for school or work. It provided respite for families, much-needed distraction for the girls and limited exercise opportunities. With only a relatively small group and counsellors specifically trained to treat anorexia, meal supervision was possible. But it would never have worked for Riche.

Nowhere I knew of catered for boys. This was where Games Workshop filled the void. It gave Riche an invaluable social outlet in the non-eating-disordered world. It distracted him from his obsessive thoughts. It put a brake on the pacing for a short while. Our visits there continued to be the only time he ever smiled.

One of the other beacons of light in addition to Games Workshop was the support Dr S, our stalwart psychiatrist, gave me during our regular fortnightly visits. Riche continued to keep his interviews short but from time to time he did indicate a problem to Dr S—his anxieties when the family visited, for example. Dr S would discuss potential solutions with me. He guided me through other problems—how to manage the conflict with the dietician, when to resist Riche's demands, how to deal with the stress of the protein shakes. He said that research had revealed the old belief that parents caused schizophrenia to be incorrect and that some day the same thing would be shown to be true of anorexia. But somehow the written word, with its message of maternal blame, exerted its hold over me. I'd developed my own special brand of Stockholm syndrome.

○

I was so tired I could hardly see the words on the page, so I closed Orbach's book and put it away. When I looked in the mirror as I undressed for bed, I finally realised that the shar pei wrinkles on my face and the slack skin on my belly owed as much to low weight as stress. I had scarcely an ounce of fat on my body.

I told Jan next time I was at the clinic. Together, we concluded that I wasn't anorexic, but I did have the difficult relationship with food that many women experienced. It's possible other eating-disorder specialists might have placed me elsewhere on the eating-disordered spectrum but whatever the diagnosis, the difference was that I had a seriously ill child and I needed to be properly fit to look after him. Jan set me up for a weekly appointment with the dietician, who devised a meal plan for me.

Gradually over the next few weeks, flesh crept onto my bones. I kept quiet about my new diet to Riche—I doubt that he noticed—and within a month I had gone up a clothing size. During one of Riche's trips to Games Workshop, I ducked into Myers to buy a pair of jeans. By now I was size twelve. Logically I knew this was not huge, but I also knew that after three pregnancies I was going to wobble like the girl in the mall if I wasn't careful. The pile of discarded jeans on the fitting-room chair grew as I ploughed on, determined to find something suitable. Eventually, I found a pair of unfashionably high-waisted jeans that acted like a denim corset. I avoided looking in the mirror as I walked around to check the fit before buying them. If my thighs bulged, I didn't want to know.

Kevin bypassed the usual pleasantries during our evening call. 'Jacqui wants to leave,' he said.

'Oh.' It was mid-May. After nearly four months, the day of reckoning had come.

'What'll we do?'

I studied the peepholes in the staircase wall and thought for a moment. The last two or three weekends Kevin, Andy and Louise had slept overnight at our townhouse—Louise on the sofa, Kevin on a bed of cushions near her and Andy on cushions in my room. Kevin and Louise took care not to venture upstairs, and conversation with Riche was of course off limits. Riche had coped well with the change in routine, a sign, I thought, that we could afford to push things further. Needed to push things further if we were ever going to live as a family again.

'Andy could move here and live with us,' I said. 'In fact, I think he should. He's getting depressed.'

Kevin sounded surprised. 'Do you want to run that by Riche?' he said.

'He'll just say no. But this may be a way to force positive change. I think he's ready.'

'And Lou?'

Pause. 'No.' Riche would tell me that because the heart is a muscle it is incapable of feeling. How then to explain the sudden ache in my chest? 'Riche's convinced she's contaminated. And I can't manage a six-year-old as well as care for him.'

'Who's going to look after her?'

I thought some more. 'What if I ask Jo?'

We talked it over. Jo, my friend who'd turned up with the iced bun, had a calm, unruffled demeanor. She was a big-hearted woman who would be happy to know she could help. She'd understand that we wanted Louise to feel secure and comfortable; she wouldn't sweat the small stuff. And Louise was good friends with her daughter Rani. Moreover Jo's house, like ours before Riche's illness, overflowed with children and animals, a situation that would feel familiar to Louise.

If Jo agreed, we'd cover the cost of Louise's care for two nights each week. I knew it was impossible to put a price tag on the intangibles Jo would provide. Kevin would somehow juggle work and childcare for the rest of the week. Neither of us considered the option of Kevin taking leave to help out. As far we knew, this nightmare could go on for years and might eat up every dollar we had saved.

The decision made, we hung up. I wasn't surprised by Kevin's news. If anything, I was impressed that Jacqui had lasted so long. Not many twenty-one-year-olds could stand the isolation of our property, to say nothing of the fleas, the family of mice who, for a while, had taken over the pantry, the carpet python that liked to drape itself over the chicken coop, and a seventy-six-year-old woman who routinely mistook the dog for her daughter.

I thought our new plan would work. Louise would be happier painting watercolours and making felt at the Steiner school than watching television in our Brisbane mausoleum. Andy was too traumatised to start at a new school, so Jan suggested that he could join the day program at Footprints. He could do his home schooling there.

When I told Riche that Andy was coming to stay, he growled. 'Does he have to?'

'Yes.'

'He can't touch my stuff. And I don't want to have anything to do with him.'

'That's okay,' I said.

This Jekyll and Hyde disease had turned Riche into his negative image. Riche wasn't just having a bad day; he wasn't grumpy because he hadn't slept well; he had actually undergone some significant internal transformation due to starvation. It wasn't his fault, but I longed to get the old Riche back, the Riche who would have said, 'I can't wait to see Andy.'

○

Time seemed to stall the following Friday, the day we'd designated for Andy's move. Riche had said nothing further about Andy's imminent arrival, but I was worried that the change would interfere with his shake routine. By late afternoon, when Kevin's car pulled up and Andy walked in with a bulging backpack and a broad grin, I too had taken to pacing, unable to settle down to either a book or my patchwork.

Andy threw his arms around my neck. I rested my cheek against his soft, feathery hair and breathed in his sweaty little-boy smell. Louise rushed passed with a brief 'Hi', keen to claim her sofa-bed. Within minutes, its lime green fabric was hidden under a blanket of soft toys, Barbie dolls, fairy wings and hair accessories. Kevin came in last, dragging a single bed mattress, which he leaned against the livingroom wall. He hugged me and kissed my lips. I pecked him back.

'Let's get this over and done with,' I said. 'I've moved my bed over. You should be able to squeeze Andy's mattress in.'

Kevin grabbed hold of the mattress. 'Is it okay if I go upstairs now?'

'Yes,' I said. 'But don't speak to Riche.'

'No.' Kevin's expression didn't alter. 'I won't.'

Kevin always expressed his love for me through actions rather than words, and even then he went for the understated approach. He would choose walking the dog in the park over a candlelit dinner and thought a mixed bunch of flowers from the local petrol station did the job as well as an expensive bouquet. Likewise, he struggled with expressing difficult emotions. He said nothing of how it felt to ask permission to go near his eldest son. And I could only guess at the depth of his pain.

○

A trip to the city was on the agenda the next morning. The boys could go to Games Workshop and Kevin would take Louise to a movie, giving me some time to myself.

'They can't come in our car,' said Riche. 'And Andy's not allowed to talk to me or come near me in the shop.'

I reassured him, and we set off in a convoy. Kevin followed me into the Myers carpark and down as usual to level P3 by the Myers' lift bank. He parked his car at a safe distance. He, Andy and Louise hung back as Riche and I made for the elevators. Louise waved at me as the doors closed between us. I waited for Andy upstairs, then I took him and Riche to Games Workshop.

Louise wanted to pay a visit to the children's section of Borders and as soon as she stepped off the escalator she spotted a soft pink teddy bear. It had a pink plastic love-heart nose, pink love-heart-lined ears, and a white neck ribbon covered with love hearts. Louise rubbed her face in the bear's fur and smiled up at me.

'I love him,' she said. 'Can you buy him for me?'

We left with the bear tucked firmly under Louise's arm. 'He's called Love Bear,' she said. 'He'll make the nightmares go away.'

Nightmares. I hadn't known about the nightmares.

○

When it was time for her to return to Mullumbimby with Kevin I helped Louise collect her belongings.

'Aren't you a lucky girl,' I said. 'You'll have two families. Rani will be like your sister.'

'I really only want to have one sleepover a week at Rani's house.' She looked very small and earnest. 'Can you come home for the other night?'

'I can't,' I said, engineering a smile. 'But I'll ring you each night.'

Louise said goodbye to Andy and then walked with me down through the garage to Kevin's car, parked on the street under a tall eucalyptus tree. The sun had sunk behind the apartment building across the road, and there was a chill in the air. I picked Louise up and buried my face in her hair while I held her close. How would this new arrangement look to her? Would she think I loved her less than Riche and Andy?

Our psychiatrist Dr S had reminded me that Louise was young. I'd have time, he said, to make things right with her. I hoped he was right. I gave her one last squeeze before I put her in her booster seat and fastened her seatbelt, just as I did for Riche. She clutched Love Bear and gave me a watery smile, and I closed the car door.

○

Each night I washed down my Zoloft tablet with a few mouthfuls of chardonnay. I had my doubts about it—asking twenty milligrams of Zoloft to hold back the flood of negative emotions was like building a dam wall out of cardboard—but at least it averted the tears. And then I rang my daughter.

One night, she told me she'd lost her first tooth the night before.

'The tooth fairy left me a dollar,' she said, unmistakable pleasure in her voice.

'Fantastic.' I slumped in my chair.

Louise chattered on. I said, 'yes' or 'really?' every so often so she'd know I was still on the line, but inwardly I was obsessing. Tooth fairy had been part of my job description, a favourite part. I remembered the elaborate notes I'd left, along with coins in coloured paper, when the boys were younger. I kept the teeth, they were all still somewhere in our cottage. The job was even more fun when the boys grew older and were in on the secret. The previous year when Andy lost a tooth I waited until Louise fell asleep and then borrowed her fairy wings and tiara and danced into Andy's room flapping my arms. He liked to say the tooth fairy had brown curly hair. Not any longer. The new tooth fairy had long, straight hair with titian highlights, was too sensible to wear wings and no doubt threw out the tooth, as I guess most people would.

At last Louise reached the end of her story and fell silent. When she spoke again, her voice quavered. 'Can't you come home, Mummy?' she said. 'I don't really want to have two sleepovers in a row, thank you.'

The politeness of this second attempt to negotiate a better deal sucked the air from my lungs. I gulped in a breath. 'Riche's too sick,' I said. I launched into my sales pitch: how great to have two families, how lucky to have Rani as an 'almost sister', but it didn't sound convincing, even to me. I gave up and told her it was time to say goodbye.

'Don't go.' Her voice went up in pitch. 'I've got something else to tell you.' My daughter paused as she scrounged around for another tale to tell, and then her little voice piped up. 'I did a good drawing today.'

She gave me a brushstroke-by-brushstroke description of a stream and a tree.

'Bed-time,' I said, when her voice petered out. 'Close your eyes.'

I closed my own eyes and settled into our nightly routine, a telephone version of the routine we used to follow in Mullumbimby.

'Imagine that you're sitting on my lap.'

We both fell silent.

'Now imagine that I'm kissing the end of your nose.'

More silence.

'Did you feel it?' I said.

'No.'

I repeated the ritual and this time it worked. Some nights it took ten minutes or so of mental hugging and kissing before Louise was satisfied. They were four-glass nights. This one was only a three.

'Okay, you hang up first,' I said, not wanting to leave my daughter yet again. The phone line went dead, and I hung up and sloshed some more wine into my glass.

The following day while Andy was at day program I threw myself into housework to overcome my feelings of self-pity. Riche's obsessive-compulsive disorder drew the line at keeping his Warhammer room clean and he hated me cleaning it, relenting only when it was filthy. As I pulled the vacuum cleaner out of the hall cupboard near Riche's bedroom, he looked up from his bed, where he was reading.

'What are you doing?'

'I'm tidying your Warhammer room.'

A look of concern. 'Please don't touch my models.'

The pungent smell of paint and glue hit me when I opened the door. I put the vacuum cleaner down and looked around. Riche had tossed empty packaging from his model kits on the floor, and a fine black residue from the spray paint that he used as a base coat had settled on every surface. Perhaps it came as a relief to him to be messy in his personal domain after the rigid control his mind forced him to exert over his actions whenever he went out into the world. But it wasn't all messy. When I peeked inside the built-in closet, I found hundreds of Riche's plastic and metal models filling the shelves, row after row of them, meticulously glued together and painted, assembled in regiments as if for battle.

I set to work, picking up pieces of cardboard and plastic bags from the floor. The paint residue gave everything a greasy feel and left black smudges on my fingers. And the desk was no better than the floor, a jumble of cardboard, paint jars, brushes and models. I resisted the urge to upset the unnatural disorder of things: Riche would be sure to know and the models would be deemed contaminated. Behind the desk, a couple of dozen models littered the floor. I knelt down to take a closer look. Some of them had hardly been touched but others looked almost finished—the details picked out with different coloured paints and sand glued on to add texture. They represented hours of work, and a fair amount of money. Confused, I went in to Riche and asked about the discarded models.

Riche's face took on a stony look. 'They've got bad memories.'

'What do you mean?'

Riche looked down and didn't answer at once. The muscles around his mouth twitched, and he looked like he would cry, but he clenched his jaw. 'I made them on bad days.'

'Bad days?' Weren't they the only kind we had?

'Days when the voice in my head said really bad things to me.' The muscles around his mouth twitched again and his eyes filled with tears.

'This voice, what does it say?' I kept my own voice as soft as the caress I longed to give him.

'Just stuff. Stuff about how bad I am, and how I'm not worth anything.' He drew his feet up to his chest and hunched forward. 'It's getting worse, Mum. I can't remember the last few days very well. They're all blurry.'

Riche's sadness settled around my heart. I was pleased that he had confided in me—it felt like a breakthrough of sorts—but my urge to clean had dissipated. I tossed the unwanted models into a bag, put the vacuum cleaner away, shut the door to the Warhammer room and went back in to Riche's room to read my book. My presence was the only comfort I could offer.

○

The next protein shake was worse than ever. Riche dashed into the bathroom part way through and made wrenching, guttural sounds as if he was trying to drag every last bit of the shake up from his stomach.

I yelled at him to stop, but he ignored me. He tipped the cup upside down and shook it, spraying thick liquid over the sink. I grabbed his arm, my fingers easily encircling the barely covered bone, and pulled—the first time I had touched him since he had flicked the blood on my walls. He held out for a few seconds before I hauled him out of the bathroom. Then I ducked behind him and stood in the bathroom doorway. When he saw that my body blocked his path back to the sink, he raised his arm and looked set to lob the shake down the stairs.

'Don't,' I said. 'You need that shake Riche. It's keeping you out of hospital.'

'It's making me fat,' he said.

I searched for a way to get through to him. 'It's nourishing your brain, Riche.' Maybe this would work. Riche valued his intelligence.

Riche glared at me, but he took a couple of sips and then stopped.

'Your brain, Riche.'

He took a few more sips. And we continued in that way until he emptied the cup. It wasn't until much later that I realised the effort it must have taken not to throw what seemed to him a poisoned chalice.

When it was time for the next shake, I took up my position in the bathroom doorway before handing Riche the cup. But fighting anorexia is like trying to flatten a balloon full of air—when one part is squashed, another part bulges. In this case, it was Riche's cheeks that bulged after a few mouthfuls.

'Swallow properly,' I said.

He made a show of swallowing, working his jaw muscles. When he emptied the cup, I demanded he swallow the mouthful he had allowed to pool inside his cheeks. His Adam's apple bobbed up and down, and it looked like he had obeyed me, but then he spat a great gob in the sink, and I realised he had shunted the fluid around his mouth and had swallowed only air.

I determined to prevent this pooling after the next shake.

'Open your mouth,' I said. 'Show me you've swallowed it all.'

Riche opened his mouth; a puddle of milky fluid covered his tongue and gathered inside his cheeks.

'Swallow again.'

He did. And looked at me with eyes full of misery.

'Show me.' I realised that my hands were on my hips, fishwife style. These standover tactics left me with a bitter feeling of self-dislike, but I had no choice.

Riche opened his mouth: it was empty. He went into the bathroom and spat over and over, and although the repeated spitting gave me a knife-edge feeling, it produced nothing but saliva.

○

It was around this time that I stumbled across a book describing Family Based Therapy, sometimes known as the Maudsley method. Developed at the Maudsley Hospital in England, this method advocates family therapy to support parents trying to achieve weight restoration (or refeeding) for anorexia sufferers at home. While the book didn't give me the reassurance I craved that parents weren't to blame for the illness, it did say that blame isn't helpful. More than that, though, it proposes that parents, when properly supported by professionals, are ideally placed to take on the project of weight restoration. FBT encourages parents to take decisions regarding food out of the child's hands. Professionals assist in working out energy requirements and parents feed their child, with nutritional advice if required.

When I first read that book I remembered the struggle over food in Mullumbimby and thought it just sounded too hard. I wondered how anyone would ever manage such an approach. Now, years later, I wonder why the parallels between it and what I was doing with Riche were so completely lost on me.

There were glaring differences too, but we'd been in Brisbane four months by the time I came across that first FBT book and in that time I had given Riche every single one of the shakes he was supposed to have, apart from the half-finished one during our not-repeated visit to Mullumbimby and the missed one after the visit to the paediatrician. In essence, I *was* refeeding him at home with some support from Sonia and more from Dr S. If I did that, I could presumably have talked him through meals. Ultimately it was the regular nutrition for his starved brain that was the key to recovery.

When I look back, I see that Footprints was on the right track: it placed a premium on weight restoration / refeeding (if at a slower rate), it insisted on medical monitoring, and it was an outpatient facility providing compassionate care.

There were key differences. FBT considers empowering parents as critical to successful intervention. I would later learn from another book, *Eating Disorders in Children and Adolescents*, that in meetings with the parents—initially weekly—the therapist 'provides information about stratagems that might work, helps parents think through options, and evaluates the success of parental efforts with an eye to identifying ways to improve results'. Individual psychotherapy to sort out any issues comes when the sufferer is well into recovery, no longer malnourished, able to think clearly and regaining independence.

Footprints, on the other hand, focused on the sufferer with intensive psychotherapy—four times a week—which was thought to train the sufferer to harness his or her 'negative mind'. Another key difference was in the emphasis Footprints placed on the dietician.

In time I would also learn that the FBT approach is the only form of intervention whose efficacy has been proven in scientific studies. It has been shown to be more successful than hospital refeeding, which has a high relapse rate. And it is, as I had always intuited, kinder to the children. (In hospitals the patients, especially younger children, are often put on general wards where the staff have no specialist training in eating disorders and may tend to consider anorexia sufferers as behavioural problems.)

I knew none of this as I sat there reading. Stress and exhaustion had taken their toll on my ability to think clearly. My information was patchy—I still had no internet access—and by then I'd read too many books that indicted me as the problem. The subliminal message was that I couldn't possibly be part of the solution.

I looked at my watch. It was almost time for Riche's protein shake. I put the book aside and somehow misplaced it, its title and the alternative path it described lost to me at a crucial time.

The billboard opposite Footprints of Angels was advertising a band called Fat City. *Perfect! Should be a huge hit with the clients.* Riche, preoccupied with his search for rogue calories, didn't see it. Was he also preoccupied by the knowledge that *The Bronte Story* was due to air on Channel 9 that night? He didn't say, and I didn't like to ask. He lifted his leg high and took a giant step through the gateway. A woman had thrown the switch on that habit a week earlier when she spilled a few ounces of her takeaway coffee. Andy and I swapped looks.

I ushered Riche upstairs for his appointment with Sonia and deposited Andy in the day room with his schoolwork, and then set off for the patchwork class that I had recently joined. Riche had agreed to stay at Footprints for an extra hour after his therapy one day a week so that I could take the class. Unable to join Andy and the girls because their food contaminated the day room, he spent the time alone, pacing in the reception area. Each time I returned for him, he looked like he'd run a marathon.

Alone in the car, I fretted. Jan Cullis had asked us to participate in *The Bronte Story*, which was a follow-up to earlier episodes that Ray Martin (from *A Current Affair*) had filmed of Jan's daughter at

Montreux Clinic in Canada. The decision hadn't been easy. How did one balance the welfare of a child and his right to privacy with a desire to fight for a better deal for sufferers and their families? There were no easy answers. And now it was too late to change my mind.

I arrived at Patches of Indooroopilly, took the last remaining seat near my friend Susan, another mother from Footprints, and displayed my antique Dresden plate sampler for inspection. It wasn't finished, but even with a chunk missing, the green, red and gold block looked, I thought, impressive. The teacher plucked at the irregular corners of my square and clicked her tongue.

'You're falling behind,' she said. 'We're starting Celtic knots today. If you don't catch up, you won't have your quilt finished by the end of the course.'

I caught Susan's eye and she grinned.

The lesson passed slowly. I was jumpy, and every thought I had led circuitously to the television program. My fingers, slippery with sweat, seemed as fat and clumsy as sausages. Two young mothers on the other side of the table chatted to each other about playgroups and nap times and what's for dinner, and I looked at them with the pity one reserves for the uninitiated.

It's all pureed peaches and cream right now. Just you wait.

○

I didn't need Jan's warning to know Riche shouldn't watch the program. Not that he would sit in the loungeroom glued to the box. Not that he *could* sit in the loungeroom. Or anywhere close to food. By now Park Street, Milton with its sidewalk cafes had become forbidden territory. If I found myself behind a food truck on Coronation Avenue I had to change lanes or drop back.

So there was no way Riche would risk greasy calories leaping out and grabbing him by the throat during a McDonald's advertisement. But even if he didn't sneak down to peek through the slits in the staircase wall, he could still hear the television.

I decided to record the program to watch while he and Andy were safely asleep. When I switched to Channel 9, however, electronic snow filled the screen. I shifted the television, gave it a good hard whack, unplugged it and switched it back on. To no avail. Meanwhile the show was about to air. I needed someone to tape it for me, but who to ask? I lived in a social vacuum in Brisbane and had never met my neighbours. I had noticed several girls going in and out of the apartment block next door, though. I'd ask them.

I climbed the steps to the girls' apartment, a blank video tucked under my arm. At the front door I could hear the soft music of girls' voices. I raised my hand then let it fall. What would I say? I willed my heart to slow and wiped my palms on my skirt, a flared Bohemian swirl of burnt orange, sage green and lilac. I liked the skirt—wore it every second day—but did it perhaps look a bit shabby? And maybe the loose-fitting embroidered shirt salvaged from my mother's wardrobe wasn't such a stylish choice. I ran my fingers through my hair. It was a long time since I'd seen the inside of a hairdressing salon.

The girl who answered my knock was the girl I would once have liked to be. Raven hair fell in soft waves to her shoulders, and her eyes, the colour of caramel, shone with intelligence. White shorts and a T-shirt showed off healthy curves and shapely tanned legs. She greeted me with the kind of smile that seems to emanate from deep inside and listened patiently while I introduced myself and asked if she could record a program for me at seven-thirty.

The girl nodded. 'You mean *The Bronte Story*,' she said. 'No problem. We were going to watch it anyway.'

The blinkers fell away for a brief moment and I glimpsed the world beyond the narrow confines of our daily routines. Real people, neighbours even, would watch the program. I handed over the video and went home. An hour was time enough to imagine thousands of people turning off their sets in disgust at the parents who publicly paraded their poor sick children. I wasn't worried about the response to Riche. He would break hearts, I knew, and give a sympathetic new face to the illness.

I opened the refrigerator and eyed the bottle of chardonnay, but resisted. I'd have to go back for the tape. I didn't want to add alcoholic breath to my bag-lady ensemble.

I picked up my latest find from Borders, *Helping Your Child Overcome an Eating Disorder* by Teachman, Schwartz and Gordic. It was well written, with lots of excellent advice, but the authors seemed to be talking about a different anorexia from the one we dealt with in Riche. They suggested regular family meetings to 'allow all members of the family to express their questions and concerns, in order to solve problems and prevent new difficulties'. The thought of the five of us sitting around a table almost made me laugh. We would need video conferencing and even then Riche would probably turn down the volume—or ask me to—when Kevin spoke. I put the book aside and turned to my patchwork. When the thread broke as I tried to untangle a knot I gave up and stared at the blank television screen. After a while, I heard the water pipes from upstairs creak and groan, which meant Riche was getting ready for bed. I waited until everything was quiet and then went upstairs to say goodnight.

Riche was in bed. The sheet, pulled up over his tatty old T-shirt, rippled as he repeatedly flexed and extended his feet.

'Lie still,' I said. 'Your body needs to rest.'

Flex, extend, flex, extend. 'Have you got the protein shakes ready for tomorrow?' Move legs up, move them back down, wriggle torso, shrug shoulders, clench and unclench fists. *The fat gremlins are coming. They're in the air. They're on her. They're all around me. Need to burn those calories.*

Riche was watching me. Impossible to know what he was really thinking.

'I'm waiting for you to go to sleep,' I mentally planted a kiss on his forehead and went to say goodnight to Andy.

Right on nine-thirty, I knocked at my neighbours' door. The

beautiful one appeared with my video cassette.

'Was there a little boy on the program?' I said.

'You mean Riche? No. Bring the video back tomorrow night. He's on then.' She must have seen advertisements—she and thousands of other Australians.

'He's my son,' I said.

I waited. The girl's face was still. Melting caramel eyes gazed at me. 'I'm so sorry,' she said. And in that instant I felt a little less isolated.

The next morning the mood at Footprints of Angels was buoyant. Callers flooded the Channel 9 switchboard after the show, and Bronte had spoken to numerous sufferers and their families in a specially set-up chat room.

Riche met Sonia for his therapy session, Andy joined the day-room group and I ducked out to the local bookshop. I found a seat in the cafe section and sipped a cappuccino, not that I needed caffeine to speed up my heart. When I returned to Footprints of Angels, I found Riche pacing in the garden.

'Can we go to Games Workshop after my next shake?'

'Sure,' I said. 'How was your session?'

'Good.'

The same old answer. Tempted to probe, I swallowed my questions although I couldn't understand why my twelve-year-old's right to privacy continued to prevail over my rights as a parent and primary carer. Sonia might discuss Riche's 'issues' for an hour four times a week during his therapy sessions, but I dealt with them minute by minute. I struggled through his protein shakes with him—and they weren't getting any easier. Despite this, my involvement with Sonia remained restricted to snatched conversations in the hallway. It was like fighting in the front line, with the weapons kept under lock and key in the war cabinet. Still, I often reminded myself, Footprints had enabled me to keep Riche out of hospital. Were saving his life with the protein shakes…along with my sanity.

We headed home and together Riche and I battled his anorexic thoughts as he sipped the next protein shake. I tended to forget that Riche battled alongside me. It was easier to see it as a struggle between his will and mine. But battle he did, each swallow of every shake representing a victory over the clamouring voice in his head.

The teeth-cleaning ritual followed the shake. It seemed to be getting worse. Riche scrubbed and spat and gargled and spat for twenty minutes while I hovered in case he vomited. He didn't. He emerged from the bathroom and after he had slipped his feet back into his sandals, was ready to set off for Games Workshop. In the city, I kept a lookout for signs of recognition due to the publicity, but Riche attracted no more than the usual number of stares.

○

That evening, after Andy and I had eaten our frozen fish and chips, I went to collect my video cassette. My raven-haired angel had tears in her eyes. She opened the screen door and hugged me. 'I was one of them too.'

She let go of me and wiped her eyes. I didn't know what to say. The curves and smile I so envied were an achievement hard won, not a genetic gift. I fumbled for words. 'How did you get better?'

'My family and my doctor talked me into going into hospital,' she said. 'I wanted to get better so I could go to university. I want to be a doctor.'

I smiled and told her I thought she'd make a great doctor.

'You'll have to come over some time, and we'll cook you dinner.'

I thanked her, knowing that the invitation would soon be lost in the details of a young and busy life. In any case, I couldn't leave Riche. And I would have nothing interesting to say. Still, it was a moment I cherished.

I reflected on her positive response to hospital treatment as I walked home. I could see it had worked for her. Maybe for many others. I just knew it was the wrong environment for Riche. Logistics alone would ensure he would be one of the patients who spent months with a nasogastric tube down his throat: no hospital could allow for the intensive one-on-one work it took to get him through his shakes.

I made sure Riche was asleep and Andy settled before I watched the video. From the moment Riche appeared on-screen, seated on the edge of the sofa at Footprints of Angels, I knew the image would never leave me. His huge eyes, circled by shadows, stared from an oyster-white face and his limbs were skin-draped bones on a shrunken frame. He was holding Bob, Jan's dog, which was a small miracle in itself. Jan had explained to Riche that Bob was in need of help because he missed Jan's daughter, an appeal Riche couldn't resist. Riche answered Ray Martin's questions so quietly that they'd had to subtitle him. Whenever the questions got too difficult, Riche bowed his head—allowing his hair, which now hung well down his back, to fall across his face—and hugged Bob closer. I thought of the teacher for gifted and talented children at Riche's Sydney school who had predicted that she would see Riche in the news some time in the future. I wondered if she was watching.

At one point, Ray asked Riche if he could walk down a street past McDonald's. Riche shook his head and reared back with an expression of terror. I doubt Ray understood the level of Riche's distress at the mention of a name that, seen through his anorexic filter, represented three of society's greatest evils: animal cruelty, globalisation and fat.

Jan joined the discussion. She asked Riche if Kevin's absence left a hole in his life. Head down, Riche nodded. Pressed further, he said in the smallest of voices, 'I'd like to fill that hole.' But how? The gap between father and son seemed insurmountable.

The camera panned to Ray, who introduced the next interview—with Kevin and me. My image on the screen shocked me. The preceding months had added ten years to my face; television cameras at least another five. And I spoke with the frantic, breathless air of a religious zealot in my bid to make people understand. Kevin, on the other hand, listened carefully to Ray's questions and his responses were calm, measured. The camera loved his strong jaw and unlined face. Despite everything, we stood close together and presented a united front for the duration of the interview.

In fact at that point we were united. I remember the interview as an ordeal we were going through together, both wanting to explain Riche's anorexia in such a way that people would understand he was sick, not just badly behaved. As we spoke, I had drawn on Kevin's strength, which he quite possibly was glad to provide.

o

Responses came in the form of letters from friends who had been unaware of Riche's illness, from strangers with warm wishes, from extended family and from two of Riche's former teachers. Kevin's family maintained their silence, seemingly unable to comprehend how much every gesture of support meant to us. I spoke to one of Riche's former teachers on the phone.

'I can't believe it,' she said. 'What can I do to help?'

I mumbled my standard 'nice to know you care' response, but Caitlin had other ideas. She wrote to Brian Jacques, Riche's favourite author. The first I knew of this was one wintry morning when the doorbell rang. A courier handed over a box with an English postmark and a Redwall Estate seal. It was addressed to Riche.

I carried the package up to my son in his darkened room. I kept the door from his room to the balcony locked to guard against suicide attempts; Riche kept the curtains shut, presumably to prevent the unauthorised entry of calories. Untidy piles of books gathered dust in the bookcase. Half a dozen half-empty Adam's Ale Pure Australian Water bottles lined the top shelf.

I held out the box. 'It's for you.'

Riche didn't move.

'I'll open it,' I said. 'My hands are clean. They won't contaminate whatever's inside.'

I opened the box and passed the enclosed book and envelope to Riche. He smiled and the room no longer appeared as dark.

'It's from Brian Jacques,' he said, his tone reverent.

He silently read the letter and then carefully refolded it and returned it to the envelope, which he tucked inside the book. He smoothed a hand over the glossy jacket and studied the illustration. The air around Riche seemed to grow very still, and his face took on a dreamy expression. I watched for a moment, scarcely daring to breathe and then quietly left.

That night, while Riche slept, I stole into his room and found the book, a signed American first edition of *Triss*, the book about the squirrel Riche had named his dog for. The letter, handwritten by Brian Jacques on *Redwall* letterhead, read:

Richard,
I hear you are one of my avid readers?

Well thanks matey, it's a pleasure to know that my work is enjoyed by someone as erudite as yourself. I also hear that you've not been too well. Don't worry about it Richard, I was in a similar position almost two years ago, and I got over it. In fact, I celebrated my 64th birthday last week. So if an old mole beast like me can make it, I'm sure a warrior as young and courageous as you will easily make it.

Keep your chin up lad, be true to yourself and good to your family—and remember,

We're all on your side Richard!

I returned the letter to the book and replaced it on the shelf. If Brian Jacques were in the room, I would have hugged him.

O

The two young mothers looked up as I took my seat at the next patchwork class.

'We saw you on TV,' one said. 'Now we know why you don't always get your homework done. It must be tough.'

○

After the television show, I noticed a subtle shift in my self-perception. With all the attention, I had become 'Riche's Mum'. I had to watch this, I thought; I needed to remember I had two other children…and a husband. Sooner or later, they were going to need more attention. Of more immediate importance, it was not in Riche's best interest that I become too enmeshed with my identity as mother of a chronically ill child. I needed to remain fluid, ready to change in response to any improvement in him. Not that there was any such sign as yet. If anything, we seemed to have reached a stalemate.

It was trench warfare, an endless battle with no tea breaks. If I'd thought about it before, I would have assumed anorexia popped up at mealtimes—a fight over food, and then on with the day. I didn't realise the illness controlled every waking moment, or that it affected every aspect of life. And each week brought new challenges. I had conquered, or had at least reached an uneasy truce with, Riche over spitting—following Sonia's advice during a hallway consultation I limited him to three spits—but who knew what lay ahead? In the meantime, I faced another weekend in early August with no Kevin or Louise until Sunday for whatever reason: a birthday party? A school concert? Every minute spent with Riche seemed indelibly imprinted on my memory, but the details of most other aspects of my life vaporised the minute Kevin told me.

On Saturday, after we had clawed our way through the morning ritual of the 4 am, 7 am and 10 am protein shakes, we headed down to the car, all of us eager to get to Games Workshop. Andy scooted into the back seat of the car. Riche, as usual, picked his way across a tripwire of invisible calories before he lowered himself into the front seat.

When we reached the Myers carpark, stage two of Operation Games Workshop swung into action. Andy and I, without ever discussing it, took our positions on either side of Riche. Our eyes swept from side to side as we searched for potential hazards. Experience had taught me that, besides the obvious hamburgers and hot chips, a bag containing cereal and tinned food or a sticky-fingered toddler could just as easily spoil our day.

Andy walked with his slender frame held taut, his face, so like my absent husband's, bent towards the ground and his arms held stiffly by his sides. I worried briefly about the effect of all this craziness on him. He wasn't a great eater at the best of times, and the statistics showed that siblings of someone with anorexia were at greater risk of developing the illness themselves.

My attention swung back to Riche. At twelve years of age, he was still wearing the same size eight trousers he'd worn the day we'd first visited Footprints of Angels six months ago. His T-shirt billowed around his torso, and his sandals looked old and shabby. His toes had worn deep depressions in the leather, but he refused a new pair. A look of fright appeared in his eyes whenever I asked, which left me wondering if this was because he feared new sandals might be contaminated by calories, or if it was because anorexia had stripped him of all sense of self worth. Maybe he thought he didn't deserve new sandals.

The usual greetings—'Champ!' or 'Riche, how are you mate?'—welcomed him at Games Workshop. Andy slipped in quietly, keeping a watchful eye on his brother. I retreated to my bench outside the store and took out my sewing. Once my patchwork classes had finished, I had put aside my sampler quilt and had started Kaffe Fassett's Leafy Rose Quilt design. I chose a mouthwatering selection of fabrics: a feast of fruits and berries in rich magentas and peacock-blues set against a verdure background. I salivated over those fruits as I was unable to salivate over the real thing, so poisoned had the whole issue of eating become for me.

The security man wandered past. We had been on nodding terms for a couple of months. 'How's Mum's taxi?' he said.

'Hanging in there.' If he looked closely, perhaps he would have seen that my fingernails were ripped and torn as I slowly lost my grip on our former life.

A short while later, I checked on Riche. The grinding thump of the music swelled aggressively through the open doorway, and the predictable heady mix of glue, paint and adolescent boy smells spilled out. Riche, a tentative smile hovering around his mouth, discussed tactics with a few other boys around one of the tables—the latest miniature battlefield with its drawbridges and slate grey cardboard edifices and shiny synthetic meadows.

Games Workshop had somehow become a calorie-free haven in his mind. It wasn't just the no-food-no-drink policy. He had recently started touching the books, despite knowing that other boys handled them. He had also taken to bringing in some of his models so that he too could game. In this store, he looked, with his stick-figure body, oversized head and long hair, like an anime cartoon that had come to life.

One day in the future, I would meet a woman in Mullumbimby who recognised me from the television show. She would tell me that during a visit to Brisbane her gamer sons had watched my son rule supreme over the table. Later, when they saw him on *The Bronte Story* they said only, 'He's a legend, Mum.' And I would weep, then and whenever her story came to mind, at the guileless spirit that looked beyond the ugliness of Riche's illness to see instead the boy who still existed beneath layers of fear and anger and incapacitating obsessions. Who knows, maybe those boys were in the crowd that day, watching as Riche lined up his warriors.

The previous week the dietician had wanted to discuss with Riche why he was able to take his Warhammer models into Games Workshop and join in with the games, when everywhere else taboos formed insurmountable barriers. This knowledge would supposedly provide the key to solving Riche's fear of contamination. He could be shown that the same principles applied elsewhere. He would be able to sit on seats, walk down the street without dodging scraps, touch people…by crikey, he might even be able to touch food.

Nice theory, but fundamentally flawed. As I was learning, very slowly, obsessions are not based on everyday logic. They involve magical thinking of the I-can't-step-on-the-cracks-or-else variety. Somehow, Riche had mentally tricked himself to make Games Workshop safe. If he were to delve too deeply into why he could touch things there the spell might break. He would lose his only pleasure in life.

Riche understood this at some level. He begged me to stop the dietician from 'spoiling it'. So I marched in to Footprints and asked that Games Workshop be left alone. The dietician reluctantly agreed, but complained to other staff of my 'uncooperative' attitude.

In retrospect, I should have refused Riche's appointments with the dietician. The weekly sessions might have been useful for some of the girls, but they weren't helping Riche. Unable to touch the door handle, he felt as if he were being held hostage, and the dietician had failed to create any useful bond with him. By then I knew my ability to get regular nutrition into Riche was more important than any chat about his relationship to food, and I chafed at the requirement.

In the future, I would read Lock and le Grange's *Eating Disorders in Children and Adolescents: A Clinical Handbook* which recommends the dietician work not with the sufferer but in consultation with the paediatrician and therapists. It also points out that no studies have been done to examine the role of dieticians.

But desperation breeds compliance. Despite the fact that I had probably come to know as much if not more than the dietician about anorexia, I continued to offer up my son for his weekly appointment, knowing that the premise was well intentioned. Although for now at least I'd kept his paint and glue kingdom out of bounds.

I had counted on a good two hours' time-out on my bench, but Riche emerged from Games Workshop after an hour, shuffling and squirming.

'Can we go? I need to go to the toilet.' The refrigerator and the toilet: the twin placentas that supplied Riche with his nutrition and removed his waste and tied him (and Andy, and me) to the womb-like safety of the townhouse.

I fetched Andy and we wove our way back across the mall, which was hamburger-free for once. Our luck held through the sunglasses and tie racks in Myers. We waited, Andy and I flanking Riche, for the elevator to arrive, and then we stepped in, all of us on full alert, ready for a possible calorie ambush at one of the lower levels. But not today: not a doughnut or ice cream cone in sight. We were home free. The lift doors opened to the familiar sight of the orange markers indicating P3, our level. Riche took his usual exaggerated step across the potentially contaminated threshold of the lift. Andy and I shadowed him as he picked his way across to the stairs that led down to our level. With the car just metres away, I allowed myself to relax. So Riche's scream from half way down the stairs caught me off guard.

'I can't go down there. I'll get fat.' He jerked and squirmed and flailed at the air like someone caught in a swarm of bees.

I looked past him and saw the french fry, two centimetres of it, squashed on the step.

'Calm down.' I glanced around to see if anyone else had witnessed Riche's outburst—he was difficult enough to manage without an audience. 'It won't hurt you. Calories from that chip can't float through the air and even if you trod on it, they can't get through your skin.' It was the old trap, the same one that had snared the dietician: thinking logic could argue with anorexia. But Riche's starved brain wasn't going to fall for logic. He knew, beyond doubt, that those calories were out to get him and that I was part of the general conspiracy to make him fat.

He hesitated, and then he appeared to realise that he had no option but to continue down. He attempted to leap the last two steps, but his sandal caught the bottom step. His foot skidded from under him and he landed heavily on the concrete floor, then screamed and staggered to his feet.

God, I thought, he must have fractured his wrist. But Riche held out his hand to show me the source of his distress—car oil smeared on his palm. I could almost see his thoughts: car oil feeds car engines so car oil contains calories. He tore at his hand and sobbed. 'Get it off me. Please get it off me. It's making me fat.'

My heart pounded so hard it seemed to fill my chest. I gulped in the petrol-fumed air as I tried to think my way through the dilemma.

'Let's get to the car. I've got tissues in the car. I'll wipe your hand.'

Riche took off, but instead of heading towards the car, he ran towards the ramp that led up to the street. He seemed oblivious to any danger from cars. Maybe he even hoped to be hit, wanted simply to obliterate his mental agony. I raced after him and overtook him easily in his weakened state. I didn't want to agitate him further, so I didn't touch him. I just blocked his way and moved down the ramp towards him, edging him down to our car. With my left arm still outstretched to block his escape, I opened the passenger door.

'Get into the car. Get in right this minute,' I said.

Riche sobbed and climbed in with his hand held away from his body. 'Please get it off me. It's making me fat. Look how fat my arm is.'

'Let me put your seatbelt on and then I'll wipe it.' I knew that once I had him strapped in, he couldn't run away because he couldn't touch his belt buckle. I fished in my bag for a tissue and reached for his hand.

'You haven't had any food in your bag have you?'

'No.' A lie. 'Never.'

I dabbed at his hand and splashed some bottled water over it.

'I'll clean it again when we get home.' I shut Riche's door and hurried to the back of the car. Andy crouched there, his face white with shock.

'That was pretty bad,' I said.

Andy nodded. He opened his mouth, but instead of words, angry sobs burst out. Tears flooded down his cheeks, his nose ran, and his body heaved. He fell against me, and I wrapped my arms around him.

Riche started as soon as I got in the car. 'I'm not having the next shake.'

I ignored him and concentrated on getting the car out of the carpark.

'You can't make me have the next shake.'

'Quiet Riche, I've got to pay.' I dug in the pocket of the car door, found the ticket, and handed it to the woman in the booth.

I hadn't even wound up the window before the next onslaught. 'I'm so fat, I'm not having the next shake.'

'I heard you the first time,' I said. 'We'll discuss it when we get home.'

'I'm not having it.'

It could hardly be called a discussion. While I scrubbed Riche's hands under the running tap in his bathroom—my touch presumably the lesser of two evils—I listened to him repeat the same thing over and over.

'I'm not having the next shake. You can't make me. You just want me to get fat.'

My gut churned at the thought of talking him through a shake. I couldn't do it. I would probably throw the damn thing at him. I went into my bathroom, splashed my face with cold water and fought back the waves of nausea. When my heart rate had slowed, I went out to Riche.

'We'll miss this shake,' I said. 'But it's not because I think you're getting fat. It's because I understand this is difficult for you.'

Was I attempting to insist that I, not Riche's anorexia, had control of the situation? Or maybe I thought an endless dribble of my words would eventually wear away Riche's stony resistance. Whatever the rationalisation, anorexia had won that round.

In time, I would come to understand that arguing with a starved brain is like flicking a switch when the electricity has been disconnected. It would take months of persistent weight restoration to re-establish the connections in Riche's brain. But I had learned by then, at least, that I had to forgive my lapses and move on.

The air in the townhouse crackled with Riche's fear and my agitation so I hustled the boys into the car and we set out for Mount Coottha Botanical Gardens. Fresh air and a change of scenery sometimes helped to get Riche back on track. But today the gardens failed to work their magic. Riche set a cracking pace, his eyes fixed straight ahead, oblivious to the beauty of the old elms and oak trees as we walked through the cold-climate section.

Andy and I glanced at each other and slogged on up the path after him. Riche's mental state showed no sign of improving. His breath came in short ragged gasps. He pumped his arms, piston-like. Every few metres he balled his hand into a fist and punched his thigh as if to punish himself for his weak and well-upholstered body. We reached a shaded grove of trees on the side of a hill. On one side an embankment cut sharply to a creek, which long months of drought had reduced to a trickle. A sweet sickly smell rose from piles of native figs, fallen from the trees above and rotting among the rocks in the creek bed. Riche stopped. He lifted a leg to climb up on the stone-walled embankment and in that instant, as I realised what he was up to, I grabbed his shirt and yanked him back with brutal force.

'We're going to the car this minute,' I said. 'And if you don't stay right next to me, I swear I will scream for help. You try to throw yourself down there and I'll have police and ambulance men here before you know it and you'll be out of my hands. They'll put you in a locked ward and force-feed you, and I won't be able to visit. There will be nothing I can do about it. *Do you hear me?*' My voice had risen to a hoarse shriek.

'Okay, okay.' Riche's voice trembled.

One part of my mind was appalled by the shouted threats; another part acknowledged that I had simply learned to use whatever leverage I had to keep him safe.

I stomped back to the car, furious at this illness that would make my son want to kill himself because of a few drops of oil on his hand. Andy, head down and shoulders slumped, looked as if he wanted to disappear inside himself. Riche walked ahead, throwing anxious glances over his shoulder at me every few seconds until we reached the car.

○

That afternoon, the walls of the townhouse closed in on me. I looked at my piles of books, my baskets of patchwork fabric and the irritatingly tasteful furniture, and I wanted to scream with the fake cheerfulness of it all, this feeble pretence of a normal life. I thought I might sneak out for a coffee if Riche had calmed down. I could see that Andy needed attention—he sat with his knees drawn up to his chest in the far corner of the sofa reading, or pretending to read—but, not for the first time, he would have to wait. I had nothing left to give. I crept upstairs and looked in on Riche. My heart plummeted when I saw him pacing round and round his room with an open book in his hands.

'Stop that. Stop it right now,' I said. 'You're listening to the anorexia soundtrack.'

Riche looked up and stared at me with dark, hopeless eyes.

'Sit down. You missed your shake. You can't afford to burn those calories.'

Riche wordlessly resumed his reading, and increased the speed of his seditious pacing. Soon he was jogging around his six-metre circuit.

'For God's sake Riche, stop or I'll…' I had no idea what I would do. Riche ignored me, his eyes glued to the page, although I doubt he was taking anything in.

I remembered the prescription Dr S had given me for anti-psychotics, and sent up thanks that I'd had it filled. If ever there was a time to give it a go, this was it. I slipped downstairs and found the box containing the medication in the pantry. It looked innocent enough. Who would imagine these paper-thin wafers contained a drug with the power to control thought? I had to slip a wafer from the foil into Riche's mouth without it touching my fingers—my sweat would dissolve the wafer—and without him realising what I was doing, because I knew he would never agree to take the Zyprexa. I dialled Dr S's mobile, seeking reassurance. After a few seconds his voicemail picked up and I knew the decision rested with me. I went upstairs to drug my son, without any idea how his body would react to the potent chemicals.

Riche looked up as I entered the room, but he continued to jog. I reached out and grabbed his arm as he passed me, and as he opened his mouth to protest, I popped the foil and released the wafer into his mouth, a high priestess with an unwilling supplicant.

'You fucking idiot.' Riche tasted the medicine and realised what I had done. The look on his face scared me, a look of demented rage that should never be seen in a twelve-year-old. His eyes blazed and he lurched at me, white-knuckled fists raised. 'I'm going to kill you, you fucking idiot.'

I broke out in a sweat and backed towards the door. 'Riche, if you kill me, who will look after you?'

'I'll kill you and then I'll kill myself.'

'Calm down.' I tried to keep my voice level, even with the blood roaring in my ears. 'It won't harm you. I gave it to you because it's not good for you to be so upset.'

I waited for the Zyprexa to take effect. The psychiatrist had told me it should make Riche less agitated, and the information leaflet in the medication box listed drowsiness as a common side-effect. I expected Riche to become sluggish; possibly to sink back on the bed. Instead, he came charging at me with his fists flailing. I could feel my breath quicken and the roaring mount in my ears. I raised my arms to deflect his blows. I felt the sting of his bony forearm catching the side of my arm. Riche backed away and started pacing around the room, still cursing, while I stood and watched helplessly.

Time collapsed in on itself. Seconds became minutes, minutes became hours. The world outside the room ceased to exist, and every detail inside it became crystal clear. The wardrobe door hung open to reveal a pitiful collection of clothes—uncontaminated ones—crammed into a wire drawer. Thick layers of dust collected on empty Adam's Ale bottles on top of the bookshelf. Riche's cherished copy of *Triss* stood at one end. Other books and magazines were piled haphazardly alongside a couple of unopened birthday presents from former school friends on the shelf below. On the far side of the room Riche's bed was unmade. Opposite me, filtered light through the thick beige curtains cast a jaundiced hue over everything.

I took a deep breath of the musty air. Riche was still pacing. His face was convulsed with anger and he was muttering, but his voice seemed to come from a great distance and I couldn't make out the words. I felt tired and heavy, wanting to leave the room but unable to make the effort to lift my feet. My throat tightened as I waited for Riche's next move; I could feel the pressure building inside my skull and wondered vaguely if this was how my mother had felt before her aneurysm burst.

When I tried to speak, the words came out in useless disjointed sentences. Riche snarled and charged at me again, swearing while he punched my upper arms. Where did he get the strength? I could hear a whimpering sound and it took me a moment to realise it was coming from me. And that was when something in my mind switched off and began to erect, brick by brick, the white wall that would close off the rest of that afternoon, swallowing several hours of memories in the process, so that all that remains are flashes of Riche's furious face.

At long last he collapsed onto his bed. I offered him water, expecting a protest, but he took a few mouthfuls from the Original Adam's Ale bottle and sank back again.

Downstairs, I threw the remaining Zyprexa wafers in the bin and sat for a while with my head in my hands. But the merry-go-round we rode never stopped. Soon I had to wash my hands and prepare for the next shake.

○

When Kevin rang that night he had no idea of the emotional shit-storm he was walking into.

'The guys are planning a surfing trip,' he remarked lightly, and the longing that rippled through his voice threatened to drag my feet out from under me. I grabbed the kitchen bench to steady myself.

'Are you fucking kidding? You're not going.'

'I didn't say I was going. I was just telling you.' His voice like sandpaper.

'You just don't care, do you?' The words flew from my mouth. 'Do you have any idea what I'm going through here?'

'Of course I do. I know it's terrible.'

'Then don't talk to me about goddamn surfing.' My face felt hot with anger. 'It's all you care about. Surfing and work.'

A breath sucked in. 'That's not true. I care about you and the kids.'

'Oh really? Then why haven't you asked how Riche is? It's the least you can do.'

'I'm *sorry*,' Kevin said, 'I'm *sorry*. I know I was a prick to Riche.'

'You don't sound like you're sorry. Can't you at least try to sound sorry?' And I raged on. I'd fallen into a routine as repetitive as Riche's protein shakes. But Kevin was, by now, a veteran of my tantrums. He seemed to understand that they came from a sense of helplessness, and his tactic was to persevere with his apologies until he hit the right tone and I relented. When he eventually asked me how the day had been, I calmed down and told him.

'He acts like he's possessed, doesn't he?' Kevin said.

'He is,' I said.

I had come to think of anorexia as an evil demon. And in truth, it possessed our entire family. Every single one of us, not just Riche and me. In many ways we were alone in this ongoing disaster. Footprints of Angels had enabled me to keep Riche at home and, through them, I had found a suitable doctor to monitor him. This had saved him from hospitalisation and quite likely had saved his life. But while we shelled out thousands of dollars for individual therapy for Riche—which seemed to make little difference with getting him to drink the shakes—Kevin and I were left with no idea of how to manage his illness as a family with a united front, bumping up against each other in a fog of ignorance and despair.

On this occasion, however, I knew where to find some stop-gap assistance. I had a couple of bottles of chardonnay tucked away in the pantry, so I pulled one out after Kevin hung up and poured myself a glass. The tepid wine going down made me wince, but after a few good swallows the temperature no longer bothered me. I settled into the gathering shadows of the night. A four-glass night.

I didn't see Andy's second meltdown. It took place at Angels, not long after the car-oil incident.

Andy loved day program at Angels. He put in a token fifteen minutes or so on schoolwork and a desultory effort with the handcrafts. So far, he had made two scrapbook pages. One featured photos of Andy in various war-like poses, wearing the Greek chiton that he and Jacqui had made before she'd left Mullumbimby. The other displayed photos of my mother on the veranda of our cottage. She's holding an echidna as she sits in her chair, a rug of orange and pink crochet squares on her lap, a look of childlike delight on her face.

In addition to the scrapbook pages, Andy claimed to have made a rag doll. I gave the doll a cursory look and said what a good job he'd done, although a close inspection suggested that Andy was unlikely to have managed the intricate sewing himself. He more likely chatted to one of the girls while she stitched the doll for him. Andy, like his father, has charm to spare, and he loved spending time with the anorexic girls. He especially loved a profoundly deaf eighteen-year-old girl and could often be found by her side on a sofa. So on this particular day, I expected to find a relaxed and beaming son. Instead, Jan greeted me with a frown.

'Andy's had a bad day,' she said. 'He got very angry at Riche's anorexia, and that opened up a can of worms.'

Memories of Scott, it turned out: a boy from Andy's old school in Sydney. Andy had struggled with learning to read. He had dyslexia which affected every area of his schoolwork: try doing maths when you can't read the problems. The school provided 'special' maths and English classes for him and two other boys. In addition to the dyslexia, Andy had poorly developed fine motor skills, so he and one other boy had 'special' sport lessons too. The word 'special' didn't fool anyone of course, especially not Scott, who teased Andy relentlessly.

'How's Andy now?' I said to Jan.

'He's fine. The girls have all been sweet. You wouldn't want to put them in the same room as Scott.' She paused. 'Look, why don't you leave Andy with us for a couple more hours? He needs a break from Riche's anorexia.'

I agreed. Secretly, I was glad that I didn't have to deal with Andy's heartbreak myself, although looking back, my lack of curiosity that afternoon amazes me. But Riche's needs swamped everyone else's. If a child is drowning in the surf, you don't take time out to help the one on the beach with the sand in his eye.

Later I would try to understand what that afternoon was like for Andy. I tried to reconstruct it from his perspective, using his memories. And that afternoon, from Andy's point of view, his brother's anorexia was like a powerful undertow that threatened to drag him under. Wanting to help, Graeme, Jan's husband, drove Andy for what seemed to him like hours around Brisbane in search of blow-up punching dolls. These were made, according to Andy, for 'fat couch potatoes with too much chest hair, so they can lean forward and beat the crap out of the doll when the umpire makes a decision they don't like'. They bought two—one for now, one for later.

For weeks, the pressure had been building inside, but Andy hadn't let himself cry: he didn't want to make things worse for his mother. She hardly ever smiled and she looked a mess. If something happened to her, what would happen to him and Riche? Now he was hot and sweaty from crying so much, and the eczema on the back of his knees itched. He tried to speak, but when he opened his mouth, he choked on his words. He stamped his feet in frustration. Someone spoke to him—a therapist or one of the girls—but their sympathetic tone only made the tears come faster. And the harder he tried to stem the flow of tears, the worse it got. *Hit the doll, Andy.* So he attacked the doll that he and Graeme had bought. It was nearly the same height as him, each punch slamming the doll's head into the floor. And each time, the doll, with its water-filled feet and blow-up body, bounced back with the same stupid expression on its face. Infuriated by the passive way the doll absorbed his blows, he punched it one more time. But this time when the doll bounced back, he kicked with all his might, connected with the doll's face and split it wide open. At last Andy smiled—a watery smile—as the air whooshed out and the doll folded in on itself and collapsed at his feet.

○

Graeme had remained in Melbourne when Jan moved to Brisbane in 2002 to establish Footprints. He had joined her a few weeks prior to Andy's bad day to replace the receptionist, who had gone on maternity leave. Riche and Andy loved him. A former basketball player, he was tall and well built with an easy grin—a masculine antidote to the clinic's florid femininity. The boys must have missed the presence of their father, although Riche would never have admitted it. Graeme did his best with both of them, taking on the unpaid role of unofficial counsellor.

When Riche told him how much he loved Terry Pratchett's *Discworld* series, Graeme bought one of the books so that he could discuss it with Riche. Now he'd bought Andy a punching doll, the perfect masculine response to a little boy's anger. I was very grateful and knew Kevin would be too, even if it felt like another man had stepped into his shoes, at least for now. That was one thing I knew about Kevin—he would never allow feelings of hurt or jealousy to get in the way of his children's needs.

When Jan and Graeme brought Andy back to the townhouse late that afternoon, Jan glanced towards the staircase peepholes before she leaned forward to whisper. 'We bought him McDonald's for dinner—chicken nuggets and fries,' she said. 'He scoffed the lot.'

Andy's eyes were red-rimmed and swollen, but he looked calm. I suppose I hugged him. I hope I did. He didn't tell me then of the ruptured plastic doll, sensing, no doubt, that the information would fail to register. Instead he asked me a question that related, as everything did for me that year, to Riche.

'Can you bring the toothpaste down?' he said. 'I've got to get rid of the McDonald's smell before I go upstairs.'

It turns out that Andy used toothpaste purely as an olfactory decoy for Riche. Unbeknown to me, he abandoned his daily tooth-brushing soon after he moved to Brisbane to live with us. When he talked about it, much later, I could hear in his ironic tone the protective layer, the carapace, that formed around his heart after that Brisbane year. He told me about the night he stood in front of the bathroom sink with his toothbrush in hand and thought, 'Fuck it. My brother's got anorexia. I've got bigger things to worry about than teeth.' He added that he swore a lot that year. I never noticed.

○

I had little comfort to offer Andy, but I did have the money to pay someone else to fill in for me. In addition to attending day program, Andy had a weekly therapy session, a weekly nutrition session, and most weeks, a one-on-one with Anna, the woman who ran the day Program. Once you factored in my session, this brought the weekly total at Angels close to $1200. Fortunately, Riche's obsessive-compulsive shopping had depleted the stock at Games Workshop, so our expense there had pulled back to somewhere around $200 per week. On top of those expenses, we continued to pay rent on the Brisbane townhouse and childcare for Louise. Kevin was hurting; I refused to consider any changes. I knew we were lucky we could afford this kind of help. Other families didn't have it so easy. One family I knew of had been forced to sell their home. I remember thinking that there needed to be a more cost-effective way of treating the illness. Which, of course, there was. But I didn't realise it then.

In the week following Andy's meltdown, his therapists put in an extra effort. The dietician included him in a food challenge at the local supermarket with the girls' group. Andy, like Riche, had always been slim and in the past this had never worried me. Now I wanted to see a good layer of flesh on him—although I didn't stop to wonder how this would happen with the strange eating-disordered meals I provided. Due in part to the deep depression that made my mind sluggish and in part to a fear of triggering one of Riche's rages, I gave Andy toast and Promite for breakfast, Birdseye fish and chips for dinner, fruit for supper, and who knows what for lunch. It didn't help that he had always picked and fussed over his food.

Jan had agreed that Andy should have some sessions with the dietician. The challenge for the girls with anorexia was to go to the supermarket and choose a 'fear' food. Andy's challenge was to choose a snack that he had never tried before. Riche remained at Angels, unable to go anywhere near a supermarket.

Andy didn't enjoy the supermarket visits much either. He later told me that as they walked along the road with traffic whizzing by, he wondered each time if one of the girls would choose that day to throw herself under a passing car.

Anna took a shine to Andy and did her best to see that he felt he was getting some attention. I was glad someone did. I can't say for sure, but I like to think that it was that week that Anna chose to take Andy to see the biggest stained-glass window in Brisbane. I feel less guilty about my neglect if I imagine him standing bathed in jewel-like colours in the quiet sanctuary of a church with his hand in Anna's.

○

In the townhouse, Andy found his own way to relieve stress. Away from his sandpit refuge at Byron Bay, he had taken to running up and down our living space while he invented his fantasy worlds, tumultuous landscapes full of monsters and demons for him to conquer. He confessed much later that the floor tiles nearly drove him mad. They were the wrong size: 'All those cracks. I kept stepping on them.' The thread of obsession runs deep in our family.

The kittens watched Andy's progress from the top level of their multi-storey scratch pole. From time to time, a grey paw would lash out at Andy as he ran past. Andy in turn batted at the toy mouse that hung from the scratch pole and which the kittens largely ignored, until one day—after another vile anorexic rage had gripped Riche— he batted the mouse with such force that it broke from its string, hit the wall opposite, and fell to the floor.

Occasionally I roused myself from my preoccupation with Riche to have some fun with Andy. We had devised quite by accident a couple of games that we played in the townhouse. The first game started one day when I walked past Andy and on impulse, stuck my right hand out and pointed two fingers at him, cocked my thumb and pulled the trigger. Andy's left hand flew to his hip but he didn't reach his holster in time.

I let my hand kick back. 'Bang! Got you!'

Andy put his fingers to his neck and made choking sounds, rolling his eyes up, as he crumpled to the floor where he writhed and moaned a bit before going stiff. A few seconds later he opened his eyes and grinned.

'You're fast,' he said. 'And you're not a bad shot.'

After that, I pumped lead into Andy on a regular basis. He could

237

never quite beat me to the draw. It always amused us although, as Andy later reminded me, I was much too tense to play if I was taking one of Riche's shakes upstairs.

The other game involved Riche's spyholes, the two rectangles cut into the staircase wall that allowed him to check up on me while I made his shakes. It puzzles me now that I didn't think to cover the holes with a few pages from one of my useless anorexia books, but perhaps the tension was worth it for the sake of our game.

One day in the kitchen I felt someone's eyes on me and looked up to find Andy's disembodied head in one of the holes.

'Somebody cut my head off,' he said, deadpan, and I laughed so much I nearly fell off my stool. Andy's head disappeared, and he rolled out from the bottom of the stairs clutching his belly as he, too, laughed. During the week following Andy's meltdown, as with every other week, we played those games several times every day. We were like children in a war zone, play-acting with wooden guns and plastic bottle grenades.

But each night, when the sun went down, demons crept out from under my bed to haunt Andy. Night after night he shifted on his mattress, unable to get to sleep. I'd drift off and wake around midnight to find him pottering around in the bathroom or sitting up, reading a comic. And during the day, when he wasn't being shot or decapitated, his anxiety showed in his watchful air and his hesitant steps, as if by treading lightly he would avoid setting off tremors in our lives.

Riche's anorexia suffered from no such compunction, as we found out on our next Friday-night outing to Games Workshop. I sat on the hard wooden bench outside, sewing, and after a while popped my head in for a routine check.

At least fifteen kids were crowded around the gaming tables—the original one and a smaller addition. Riche stood slightly apart from the group. We'd been in Brisbane seven months now and his hair reached his waist and hung over his face in an ash-blonde sheaf. He looked like a shrunken Gandalf. Games Workshop was the one place where something, either a remnant awareness of social conventions or total intellectual engagement, stilled his legs. Other kids sat at the painting tables with their pots of paint and their finely bristled paintbrushes, and the place buzzed with youthful enthusiasm. I decided to duck off for coffee.

The customers in the Borders coffee shop seemed half anaesthetised compared to the gaming kids. Vague figures lounged in the easy chairs, flipping through magazines or chatting in conspiratorial tones. I sipped my cappuccino, nibbled my raisin toast and let the muzak wash over me.

On my return, I spotted Andy hovering, magazine in hand, near the front of the store. He looked over and saw me, and I got the impression he'd been waiting for me because he dropped the magazine on the front counter and hurried out.

'Riche's covered in blood, he looks totally weird.' Spit gathered in the corners of his mouth as he rushed the words out. 'Can you get him out of there?'

'Slow down,' I said. 'What happened?'

'He's scratched the backs of his hands so much they're bleeding. He's wiping the blood all over his shirt and pants. Everyone's freaking out.'

Riche was standing in the back of the store behind the larger gaming table. I walked part-way into the store and beckoned him over. As he came closer, I saw his blood-stained clothing. His hands and forearms, too, were covered in blood. He looked at me with a worried expression on his face.

'Do we have to go?' Another wipe of the hands. 'It's a great game.'

'Your hands.' His lack of awareness floored me. 'You're covered in blood. What happened?'

Riche examined his hands. Months of obsessive washing had left the skin looking like a lunar landscape. 'Oh,' he said. 'They started bleeding. I had to wipe them.'

One of the staff came over. 'We wanted to put Bandaids on,' he said. 'But Riche wouldn't let us.'

My face felt hot. 'Sorry. I'll take him home.'

Outside I spoke to Riche, my voice harsh. 'Do you have any idea how you look to other people?'

I hated the stares and whispers we regularly encountered, and I hated that I cared what anyone else thought. At the entrance to Myers, I told Riche to stay close to me and to avoid the merchandise.

'We're sticking to the central aisle,' I said.

'What if someone's got food?'

'Pity you didn't think of that before you wiped blood all over your clothes.'

Perhaps the intensity of my distress warded people away as we trundled through Myers, for we made it home safely. And there a subdued Riche washed his hands and submitted to bandages—taken from their sealed wrappers while he watched.

One morning two or three weeks later, Riche came into my bedroom to wake me for his first shake. Groggy and exhausted, I rolled over to check the clock. It was 3.30 am. Definitely a battle worth picking.

'No way,' I said. 'Too early.'

Riche whined and begged, but I remained firm. 'And since you've woken me up,' I said, 'I'm not giving you the shake until 5 am. I don't want to crash the car today because I'm half dead. I need my sleep.'

'That's too late.'

'Too bad.'

'I won't drink it.'

'You don't get a choice.'

I kept my heels firmly dug in to the warm bed sheets. After ten minutes or so Riche retreated, and I reset the alarm and went back to sleep. And with that, another switch was thrown. Five am became the new obsessive start to the day. Up until now, I'd often felt as if I were riding in the passenger's seat with Riche's illness in control. Not this time. For once it was me, not my son's illness, in the driver's seat, and I had my hands firmly if exhaustedly on the wheel.

Ground down by the merciless despot that was Riche's illness,

I never took stock of my progress with him. If I had I would have realised I was beginning to get the hang of how to manage his obsessions. I had learned to wait until the right opportunity presented itself to initiate a change, then I made my voice firm. I had to sound as if I meant what I said and believed it would happen. It helped to envisage myself as a gentle giant—kind but implacable. The same process worked with giving the protein shakes and would, presumably, work one day with food.

Each change was like reprogramming—it cancelled the previous behaviour. Each small victory helped restore my confidence in my mothering abilities, so badly undermined by most of my reading and, unintentionally, by my exclusion at Footprints, where I was given the impression that Riche's five sessions each week with Sonia and the dietician were essential to his recovery.

This was not a deliberate attempt at misinformation. The Footprints therapists showed unfailing devotion and compassion with difficult clients. The clinic's insistence on regular nutrition was critical to Riche's well-being and enabled me to keep him out of hospital; their requirement for medical monitoring was exemplary. Jan would, within weeks, hold parent information evenings in an effort to increase our understanding of the illness. There was as yet no widespread knowledge of other, more parent-inclusive approaches to treatment, and I still believe Footprints presented the best option available to us in Australia at the time.

But daily psychotherapy was unnecessary and of questionable use to a starved brain—quite apart from the fact that, for families less fortunate than ours, it would have been financially unviable. Moreover, I was beginning to suspect I could play—was playing— more of a role in Riche's recovery than I had been led to believe. I'd weathered the blood-test crisis and, later, the far worse car-oil crisis alone. And this perhaps was where the tide had started to turn. It's hard to be sure. But I began to realise that I could handle anything this wretched illness threw at me, that I might even manage the crises better than a stranger because I knew Riche so well: I was his mother.

There had been the odd chink of light before, and certainly there were challenges still to come but *anorexia was not getting the better of me*. Riche was taking his protein shakes and drinking water, his weight was very slowly increasing, and he was coping with having the rest of the family in the apartment, even if two members were relegated to the downstairs area. His social engagement at Games Workshop continued to improve.

There was a long road ahead. Now, however, I finally began to see a return to our home in Mullumbimby in under five years as a possibility.

○

But the constant stress was taking its toll on my body. After five days of a mild cough and dripping nose, I woke one Saturday morning in late September with a burning forehead and a dry throat. My chest ached and felt heavy and congested. When I heaved myself to an upright position, the room tilted and swayed, so I slumped back against the pillows. I coughed—a deep, rattling cough that produced some nasty green gunk. I knew what that meant: I'd had pneumonia before. This time I would take myself off to a doctor quick smart because last time my delay cost me a week in a Sydney hospital, and I could ill afford that.

I groped under the pillow for a tissue and spat into it. Then I sat up again, slowly this time, and waited for my head to clear. The cats lay curled together at the end of the bed. One opened his eyes and watched me for a moment before he yawned and went back to sleep. When the dizziness had passed, I swung my legs round and climbed out of bed, taking care to avoid Andy, asleep on his mattress on the floor. My coughing must have disturbed Riche because he appeared at my doorway, wearing his sleep-rumpled grey trousers and environmentally aware T-shirt. His anorexia-induced phobias were at least saving me a small fortune in pyjamas.

'It's five o'clock,' he said. 'Can you get my protein shake?'

'Sure.' I coughed. 'Let me just wash my hands.'

As soon as we had finished with the shake and its accompanying rituals, I went into my bathroom and peeled off my sweat-soaked pyjamas. When I leaned against the shower wall and let the steaming water run down my body, the hot water triggered another coughing fit that bent me double and left me limp. I had wanted to keep Riche and his fear of floating calories away from the medical system, but I would be happy to seek help for something as non-controversial as a nice gob of phlegm.

Pneumonia or not, we still had to get through the day. The doctor would have to wait until after Games Workshop. By midmorning, we were in the familiar surrounds of level P3 of the Myers carpark. I took care of Riche's seatbelt and door handle. In eight months, their contaminated status hadn't changed. We walked to the flight of stairs that took us up to the lift bank on the floor above. At the base of the stairs, Riche stared at the patch of ground where, weeks earlier, the oil spill had contaminated his hand. He circled wide to the other side of the stairs and focused his eyes on the step that had harboured the squashed chip, his gaze so intense it was as if he were shining UV light to reveal the faded outline of a crime scene. He negotiated the first two steps normally but skipped the irretrievably contaminated third step by lengthening his stride.

At the top of the stairs Andy and I took up our positions on either side of Riche, ready to ward off incoming hamburgers or Coca Cola cans. We made our way between the rows of parked cars towards the lift. Once inside, Riche moved to the back, stopping short of the wall and its invisible wallpaper of contaminants. At each level people stepped in and turned to face the doors. Riche stabbed their backs with his eyes while I did my best to contain my coughing. Then the lift stopped at the food court and a young child with a hamburger got in.

Riche's gaze homed in on the hamburger. His body went rigid; the muscles of his face formed a matrix of fear.

'Look at me,' I said, still quixotically giving rational discourse my best shot. 'Calories don't travel through air.'

But Riche was beyond hearing. His face twisted, and he clutched at his scrawny neck and writhed in the corner of the lift. His eyes brimmed with tears and muted strangling noises escaped his lips. Heads turned and then turned away, embarrassed by such unaccountable public distress. No one laughed. I moved closer to Riche and spread my arms, a human shield between my son and the killer calories in the hamburger. Andy assumed guard on the other side. Unconcerned, the child sank his teeth into his hamburger. Riche groaned and squeezed harder at his neck.

'Stop it!' I hissed the words at Riche.

The door opened at level Q, the ground floor of Myers store, and the lift disgorged the hamburger and most of the shoppers. I held the lift door open, taking care to avoid the eyes of the remaining occupants, and waited for Riche. But he hung back.

'Come on,' I said. 'You've got to get out. The kid with the burger has gone.'

Andy stepped out of the lift and assumed sentry position while Riche got out, taking his usual giant step over the metal grid. He stopped at the entrance to the Myers tie department and scanned the path ahead. The hamburger kid was nowhere in sight, so Riche picked his way past the cabinets of rolled ties and between the racks of hanging ties. Andy and I must have looked like a presidential bodyguard with our practised watchfulness and our take-no-prisoners approach to junk food.

And then we were on the escalator going up to Games Workshop, and two hours of freedom for me.

It seemed only minutes had passed and it was already eleven-thirty: time to return to the townhouse for the next protein shake. And then I would call Graeme. The system wasn't perfect but I could depend on Jan and Graeme to help in an emergency. I knew Jan had flown to Melbourne for the weekend, but Graeme might be free to sit with the boys while I went to the doctor. They could talk Terry Pratchett or pummel Andy's spare punching doll. When I rang Graeme, he told me he was out of town, visiting friends. He could come back if I needed him.

I declined and hung up. I rang Kevin in Mullumbimby to let him know. He offered to drive up but again I declined. The boys would be fine for a couple of hours.

When Riche had finished his two-thirty protein shake, I went downstairs and picked up my purse and car keys. Andy was reading a comic book on the sofa.

'I'm going to the Emergency Department at the Wesley Hospital—that's the closest,' I said. 'I'll call you. Can you keep an eye on Riche for me?'

Andy looked up from his comic book. If he was uncomfortable with the role of caretaker-child, his level hazel eyes didn't show it. 'Will you be okay?' he said.

I gave him the thumbs up and went upstairs to tell Riche.

'Who's going to look after me if they make you stay in hospital?' he said.

'I'm an adult,' I said. 'They can't make me. I'll be home soon.'

Riche started tapping his foot. 'My next shake is due at four-thirty,' he said. 'You won't be late, will you? I'm not having it if you're late.'

○

Hospital bound on Coronation Drive, I looked at my watch: I had a little over an hour. The last two shakes of the day were particularly difficult, being close together, but I'd learned not to mess with Riche's schedule.

I turned the corner to the Wesley Hospital. My stomach pitched and rolled at the familiar sight. This was the scene of the 'fuck you' visit to the paediatrician and numerous encounters with Trish the blood technician. I'd been told this hospital was also where Rebecca, whose mother had donated the use of the premises for Footprints of Angels, had died only four or five years previously. The Emergency Department was in a different wing, though. I checked in with the receptionist and then found a public telephone so I could call Andy. He sounded calm. Everything at home was fine. How was I? Would I be long? Riche was making Warhammer models. Andy had been allowed over the threshold to watch—a jaw-dropping first.

I had timed my visit to beat the Saturday afternoon peak hour of sporting injuries, so I didn't have long to wait. A nurse led me into a cubicle and a brisk young male doctor appeared. He asked a few questions, nodded when I told him why I needed to get home, listened to my chest with his stethoscope and filled out an X-ray request form.

Half an hour later, I stood with him in front of the X-ray light box. The doctor took a pen from his coat pocket and pointed at some cloudy white markings on the film. 'Some shadowing at the base of the left lung,' he said. 'Right here. I think you've got a touch of pneumonia, but it's not severe. I'll give you some antibiotics—a cephalosporin—and you should be right to go home. Come back if you're getting worse.'

I thanked him, checked my watch as I settled the account and let Andy know I was on my way home. According to him, Riche was wearing tracks into the carpet on the upstairs landing waiting for his next shake, which was due in ten minutes. With light traffic and a heavy foot on the accelerator I made it with a minute to spare. The medical system had earned its keep this time.

○

Jan greeted me with an anxious smile at the clinic on Monday morning.

'Graeme told me,' she said. 'Pneumonia?'

I nodded. 'Yes. But the antibiotics have kicked in.'

'You gave us a fright,' Jan said. 'It's time we got Riche to take his shake from someone else. Otherwise we'll be in trouble if you get really sick.' Her face took on a determined look. 'I'll come round to your place one day, and I won't leave until Riche's taken a shake from me. He's not going to like it.'

'All right. If you think it's a good idea.' I could feel an ache developing behind my eyes. I didn't really need Jan's warning that the experience would be unpleasant.

She went on, suggesting it might be better for me to leave her alone in the townhouse with Riche. Andy, certainly, must not witness Riche's negative mind in top gear. It could take hours. Cups might be thrown. Riche would rage. I baulked at the prospect of more confrontation for my son and pleaded with Jan to wait.

'A week or two,' she said. 'But we've got to do it.'

Jan was right. Moreover, the timing seemed right: Riche's obsessive-compulsive questions about the shakes had definitely lost some of their sting. They'd started to sound more like a habit, like a worn but loved pair of slippers. On reflection, I thought Riche could probably cope if someone else's hand replaced mine as the hand that presented the shake. But the person I had my eye on for the job was Graeme.

Graeme's Terry Pratchett spree had paid dividends. He had also made a visit to Warhammer one Friday night to watch Riche take part in a game so that he was able to discuss it knowledgeably with him. As intended, he'd earned Riche's trust. They chatted each day for at least an hour—Graeme related to Riche as one of the guys, not as a psychologist. Riche, meanwhile, told me that Graeme helped him far more than the dietician; more, even, than Sonia. 'We talk about all kinds of stuff,' he said. 'He makes me feel normal.'

It made sense. After eight months, the dietician had still not managed to establish any rapport with Riche. He didn't seem to have Graeme's knack of showing an interest in Riche's hobbies. Perhaps if he had learned something about Warhammer before he tried to embark on a discussion of why Riche could touch things at Games Workshop, he might have got somewhere. Perhaps not. Logic didn't have a great track record with Riche's anorexia.

Sonia maintained a good relationship with Riche. On one of the few occasions Riche divulged the contents of their discussions he told me they had shared interests in dogs and architecture. The other person who had reached out to Riche, during a visit to Footprints, was Bronte Cullis. She introduced him to a war game called Risk and played it with him a few times, before she left and the game was put aside.

But when all was said and done, Bronte and Sonia were female. It was Graeme who had the goods. So when he stopped by our townhouse to say hello a week or so later, I saw my opportunity and asked him if he was up for the challenge.

Graeme nodded and grinned. 'Sure. I'll have a go. What's the drill?'

'Wash your hands thoroughly,' I said. 'That way you're telling the truth when he asks you. The fewer lies, the better…' I took Graeme through the routine: hygiene, recipe, Riche's FAQs. 'Got all that?'

Graeme rubbed his hands together. 'I think so.' He rolled up his sleeves.

I pointed to the kitchen sink. 'You can scrub up there. I'll tell Riche what's happening.'

Riche was in his Warhammer room, standing at the desk as usual, painting a model.

'Time for your shake, buddy,' I said. 'Graeme's going to give it to you. He knows the rules.' Riche paused, paintbrush in hand, and opened his mouth. I went on smoothly, 'Wash your hands and Graeme will be up in a minute.' Riche turned back to his desk as if this were an everyday occurrence, like toothbrushing.

Andy was on his mattress reading a comic book. I told him the plan and asked him to stay put. Then I went back down to Graeme, told him I was going out for a coffee and left.

○

The cappuccino machine hissed, and the rich aroma of the grind filled the cafe. I licked the last crumbs of lemon tart from my spoon and wondered how Graeme was faring with Riche. After eight months of stress five times every day the sheer relief of someone else taking responsibility for feeding him left me lightheaded. Exclusive feeding rights were never my goal. That had evolved mainly as a product of Riche's acute anxiety, and probably mine too. Riche's weight gain had stalled. His total gain, the dietician admitted, was around 4.8 kilograms, and he needed every single protein shake to prevent the weight loss that would jeopardise his ability to remain at home. Not wanting to upset the balance, I hadn't pushed him to accept his shakes from anyone else. But I longed for Graeme to succeed. It would signify the loosening of one more obsessive-compulsive bond, and being relieved of my duty, even just once or twice a week, would make my life more bearable.

○

Graeme greeted me with a broad smile on my return. 'He took it like a lamb.'

I stared at Graeme. Did he see a mixture of relief and astonishment in my eyes? Did he see joy and gratitude? After all these months of solo responsibility for Riche's shakes, I was good at concealing my emotions. But now, although I tried for a composed demeanour, I felt as if they were practically bursting out of me. Someone else had endured the skull-shattering tedium of giving Riche one of his protein shakes. It had seemed as if that day would never come.

I thanked Graeme and let him out the front door and then sat for a long time on the sofa, staring out of the window at nothing. The walk had tired me. It was a lingering side-effect of the pneumonia, but pneumonia had turned out to have the unexpected and very welcome additional side-effect of Riche taking a shake from someone else. I had no plans to get sick again but at least I knew that if I did, Riche wouldn't need to go to hospital. Further, the whole incident served as a reminder to me to stay alert for opportunities to force change, to gouge away at the remaining obsessive-compulsive rituals that trapped Riche as surely as any padlock.

For despite a few brighter signs lately, change was still sorely needed. In the week following Graeme's victory Riche reached 29 kilograms. The fiftieth percentile weight for boys at twelve years of age is, according to the charts, 40 kilograms. Judging by the few early childhood height and weight records I had kept, Riche should have weighed around 36 kilograms, throw in an extra kilo or two for a safety margin. He had grown a couple of centimetres since our move to Brisbane, but in that time Andy, who was short for his age, had shot up past Riche. This meant that Riche wasn't taking in enough nourishment to support normal growth.

The dietician had no answers, despite continuing to meet with my reluctant son on a weekly basis. Certainly, there had as yet been no suggestion of increasing the number or strength of the protein shakes, the calorie content of which I remained ignorant. The general consensus seemed to be that Riche needed to tighten the reins on his negative mind, whatever that was, before he would be ready for the challenge of food. Riche continued to pace the six-metre circuit in his room whenever he could, and so, unsure of what else to do, I decided to clamp down on that habit.

'You need to stop pacing,' I said to Riche. 'It uses up valuable energy. You're stunting your growth. Do you want to end up really short?'

'No.' He looked scared.

'And your brain won't develop properly.'

This was my ultimate argument, the only use of logic that occasionally seemed to crack the eating-disordered barrier in Riche's brain, although these days, unlike before, slenderness usually seemed to rate higher than IQ.

But in fact I was only guessing about that. I couldn't see Riche's thoughts, and he rarely expressed them. I no longer knew if he believed he was fat, or if he was just powerless to break the horrible cycle of obsessive behaviour that trapped him. Not that it made much difference to the outcome. If he continued this way he would end up stunted, with brittle bones, internal organ damage and a poor education. But at least he wouldn't be fat.

I was not the only one concerned with Riche's failure to gain sufficient weight. Jan approached me one day while I was waiting for Riche to emerge from his therapy session.

'The dietician has found a high-energy supplement for Riche to take,' she said. 'It's a fatty acid solution. Riche needs to take a dessertspoonful each day.'

'Great,' I said. And about bloody time. After four thousand dollars worth of appointments, the dietician should be coming up with some ideas. But I could see problems with the name. 'Riche's not going to want to take anything that's called "fatty".'

'I know,' Jan said. 'We'll have to tell him it's a vitamin and mineral mixture. I'll take the label off the bottle, so he doesn't know what's in it.' A mischievous sparkle crept into her eyes. 'You know what? I'll tell him the mixture contains growth hormone from a Himalayan yak.'

She laughed and I laughed with her, but the laughter made me uneasy. It felt disrespectful. I hated to make fun of Riche's illness in any way, and although I told lies to make life easier for him—somehow maintaining the fiction that the supermarket shelved its soymilk in isolation from all the other products—I tried to stay as close to the truth as I could.

Jan handed me a large clear plastic bottle of the fatty acid solution later that week. It looked like an antacid medicine: thick and milky. Someone had scribbled over the label with marker pen. Neither Riche nor I, as it turned out, would know the calorie content. In the garden, Riche looked at the bottle and I waited for the barrage of complaints.

'Jan said it's got growth hormone in it,' he said. 'Extracted from

Himalayan yaks. If I drink it, I'll get taller. I'll catch up to Andy and overtake him.'

Perhaps Jan was right. What did it matter as long as Riche drank the stuff? 'That's great,' I said. 'You can have the first dose when we get home.'

'It won't make me fat, will it?'

'I promise it won't make you fat.'

○

When it was time for the first dose I rattled off my well-rehearsed speech, repeating the words 'vitamins and minerals' and 'grow taller' several times in a firm voice but drawing the line at Himalayan yaks, and held out the spoon with a confident hand. Experience had taught me that Riche would open his mouth and meekly accept the tablespoon of solution that I tipped in. If he took it once he would take it again. The fatty acid solution would soon become part of the obsessive-compulsive routine.

And it did. Each day, he opened his mouth without protest and allowed me to feed him. Jan's yak story bothered me even though I hadn't mentioned it, mainly because it seemed an unnecessary lie. So on the fifth day, when the routine was well established, I told him that the mixture was in fact ordinary vitamins and minerals, which, among other things, it was. Riche gave me a blank look as if to say 'who cares', swallowed the solution, and returned to his Warhammer models. The switch had been well and truly flicked on this new routine.

Over the next few weeks, his weight remained the same despite the fatty acids, but his mental state improved. He ran through the same list of questions with each of his protein shakes, but without urgency. He kept swilling the shake around the side of the cup, but he made no serious attempt to tip it out. And one day at the clinic, one of the girls with anorexia stopped me with a huge smile. She told me Riche had ventured part way down the internal spiral staircase in order to listen to the weekly 'values' discussion rather than taking up his usual position, poised for flight at the outside door. She sounded so proud of Riche.

I thought about the orthodoxy that dismissed anorexia as either vanity or an attempt to control. Had any of these old-school experts ever met a sufferer? When I ever had a moment to take a step back from all the stress and tedium, I found myself awed by the girls' compassion and the courage with which Riche battled the disease. Even when he seemed to be doing more losing than winning.

I watched the woman. She rested her elbows on the black granite of the kitchen bench, the smooth grey plastic of the telephone pressed hard against her ear. Deep lines furrowed her forehead, tiredness—anger?—clouded her eyes, and the mass of brittle corkscrew curls springing out from her head gave her a slightly crazed appearance. She kept her back to the staircase and spoke quietly so that her sick son upstairs could not hear her, but there was no mistaking the venom in her words. Who was this woman with the hectoring voice? I knew I needed to extract her from her snarl of words, but I felt powerless to stop her.

It was me, of course. Part of me was having a conversation with my long-distance husband and part of me was watching, curiously detached and more than slightly horrified by what she saw and heard. Kevin was pressing his case.

Merrill Lynch held a New York conference for Australian clients each year. If he continued to work for Merrill, he needed to attend. It was part of his job. I liked the lifestyle, didn't I? (Lifestyle? What lifestyle?) Okay, so now wasn't such a good time to mention lifestyle, but I knew what he meant: the expensive holidays, the designer clothing. He'd seen the Visa account. (Oh yeah? Well if you were in my shoes, you might at least want them to be good shoes, and anyway we're not exactly talking Manolo Blahniks.) Well then, what about the property near Mullumbimby? (Oh, you mean the one I no longer live on?) But that's only temporary. Riche won't be sick forever. (Sure as hell feels like it.) Come on honey…

We argued back and forth, but much as I resented the fact that he needed to be at the New York conference, I knew it to be true, and so I conceded, with as little grace as humanly possible, that he did indeed need to go. Merrill Lynch had been good to us over the years but it was an investment bank, not a benevolent society.

Kevin sighed; I opted for a long-suffering silence.

Kevin, too, lapsed into silence, but I could as easily out-silence him as out-talk him, and after a long moment in which I imagined him squirming uncomfortably and looking longingly at the ocean, he caved in and spoke, brisk and business-like. He had closed the deal, now for the details.

'What are we going to do with Louise?' he said. 'Can she stay with Jo for the whole time I'm away?'

'Don't be ridiculous.' I wasn't quite ready to climb down from the moral eyrie of She Who Has Made the Concession. Moreover, I was tired, a tiredness that permeated through to my core, a tiredness that slowed my brain and weighed down my limbs, a tiredness that never left me.

If Kevin were to go away, I would need to pick up the slack with Louise in Mullumbimby, at least visit her several times. That was do-able; I'd ventured down for a quick visit with the boys several times in recent weeks. We headed off after Riche's therapy, stayed a couple of hours and returned to Brisbane—five or six hours in all. Riche tolerated a protein shake on the side of the Pacific Highway or in our garden, depending on our schedule. But several times in one week? How would I cope with all the driving, and then the demands of an energetic six-year-old?

So although I knew the answer to his question, I let him stew:

'You'll be away for a full week. It's far too long for her to spend at Jo's. She's barely coping with two nights a week.'

Kevin made small noises meant, presumably, to indicate thought but more likely indicating that he had absolutely no idea what to do. I waited. Eventually, Kevin spoke. 'Can she go up and stay with you for a few days?'

'Won't work.'

More thinking noises. I began to feel ashamed of myself. The isolation, the loneliness, the uncertainty of Riche's illness were eating away at me. Adversity was turning me into a person I didn't want to be: mean spirited and childish. *If I can't have fun, why should you?* I considered the unfamiliar proposition that Kevin might feel bad about this too. Perhaps it wasn't as easy for him to drop everything and check into the Qantas first-class lounge as I imagined. Perhaps he did regret leaving me to juggle things on the home front for a few days. Perhaps it was time for me to stop being a first-class harridan.

I stood up from the kitchen bench and took a few steps. Then with more effort than Kevin would ever know, I forced myself fully into the present moment and the task of figuring out a solution. I thought of the caravan we'd bought a couple of months before I'd moved to Brisbane. We'd never used it.

'Don't worry,' I said. 'I'll go down to Mullumbimby and stay with her for a couple of nights to break it up. She can spend the rest of the time with Jo.'

Kevin sounded incredulous. 'But you haven't stayed overnight since you moved to Brisbane. Riche won't even go into the cottage.'

'I think I can get him to stay in the caravan. Andy and Loui and I will sleep there with him. It's too far from the house to leave him alone.'

'Won't he think the caravan's contaminated?'

'No. He's never seen us eat in there, and we'll tell him the previous owner always ate out. There's a catch, though: we can only stay one night at a time because Riche won't have a toilet he can use. He'll be able to pee outside, but without a flushing toilet and a bathroom sink, he'll end up constipated. We'll go down on Tuesday afternoon and stay Tuesday night. Louise can stay with Jo on Wednesday, and we'll go back down for Thursday night. The other advantage to that plan is that Riche won't go too long without seeing Sonia.' There were also the cats. I could leave them for one night with food and water, but not longer.

'What about his shakes?'

'There's a small beer fridge in the caravan, isn't there? And I'll buy a blender to keep there. Then I only need bring down enough powder, soymilk and strawberries for a night.'

'Think it'll work?'

'It has to. In fact, it'll provide the perfect excuse to trial a night with Riche at home. It'll be a step in the right direction if we can pull it off.'

I sat for a while when we'd finished talking. It was October. Christmas was in two months. Would that be time enough to ease Riche into staying in the caravan for several nights at a stretch, making do with a bush toilet, or would Andy and I be stranded in this wretched townhouse on Christmas Day, reduced to Birdseye oven-baked fish shapes (with lemon crumbs—knock yourself out!) and frozen chips? Kevin would be inundated with invitations to join other families for Christmas lunch. People assumed that a man alone should be looked after, whereas a woman alone could manage. (There it was again: that Scrooge spirit creeping back in whenever it saw the chance.)

Riche grumbled when I told him the plan but gave in surprisingly easily, just as he had when I had told him I wanted to leave him at the clinic for a couple of extra hours once a week so I could take a patchwork class. Changes in his routine seemed easier to bring about when tied to a specific need. It provided one of those opportunities I was always on the lookout for. It might have been that the need gave steel to my words, or maybe it was because Riche found it easier to change when the need was external to him. He still wanted, desperately, to please me in situations that didn't specifically involve his protein shakes—as if he knew what a nightmare they were and wanted to make amends.

The following week I packed the boys and Riche's supplies into the car, along with a talking book of John Marsden's *Tomorrow* series. Before I reversed out of the garage I put on the first tape and, as we set off for Mullumbimby, we listened to the story of a group of teenagers who returned from camp to find their hometown occupied by an invading force. A surprise attack and invading forces: these were familiar concepts to me.

The dogs rushed out when they heard my car, but I didn't stop. I drove past our cottage and under a towering handkerchief tree to the caravan, fourteen metres of uncontaminated living space next to the rainforest trailhead.

Riche looked at the caravan. 'Are you sure it's clean?' His voice trembled. 'Are you sure there's never been any food in there?'

'Absolutely,' I said. 'The last owner told me he never used the stove. And he didn't take the plastic off the seat cushions, so we know they're clean.'

'Does Louise have to sleep in the caravan?'

'When you were six, you wanted to be near me. Louise does too.'

'Will you keep her out of my end of the caravan?'

'Yes,' I said. 'Time for your protein shake.' I wondered if Riche heard the tiredness in my voice. 'I brought some Adam's Ale to wash your hands.'

Under Riche's watchful eye, I took the cooler from the back seat of the car and carried it into the caravan. It smelled of disinfectant and the bench tops sparkled. Kevin had done a lovely job. I unpacked the cups of protein shake and put the three of them—enough to last until our return to Brisbane—into the refrigerator. As back-up, in case Riche tossed the shakes, I'd brought a spare box of protein powder, a punnet of strawberries and a carton of Sanitarium no-fat soy.

Next, I went back out and took the liquid soap and a bottle of water from the car. I squirted soap onto Riche's hands, he rubbed them together, then I poured the water to rinse them off. That done, I went back into the caravan to fetch a protein shake. As I did so, I tried not to dwell on the ridiculous complexity of the operation. All for the sake of a few miserable millilitres. Riche took the cup from me and added a few questions to his usual list. Was the caravan clean? The cooler didn't get too close to Andy in the car did it? I didn't have anything bad in the car, did I? Was I sure, really sure, that the caravan was clean? Louise hadn't touched anything, had she? When I had sufficiently perjured myself, Riche took a few sips.

I breathed in the sweet air and let my gaze drift off to the trees. In that instant, my eye caught a flash of movement. Riche had upended his cup and, in the split second it took for me to react, was vigorously shaking it, so that drops of protein shake sprayed out through the straw and onto the ground. I thought the lid would come off but, miraculously, it didn't. And it didn't seem to occur to Riche to take it off himself. Or maybe—I wondered this later—he hoped I would intervene before he did, to stop the behaviour he knew he couldn't. I yelled at him to tip the cup the right way up. He shook it harder. I threatened to make him drink another shake if he didn't stop wasting this one.

What a terrible illness. It never let up, not even for one shake, and the only language it seemed to understand was threats. If I had offered Riche a thousand dollars to drink that shake, he would have turned me down. As it was, he righted the cup and took another few sips. Then he started to tip the cup again.

'Don't even think about it; there's plenty more where that came from.'

Every cell in my body moved to standby. This plan had to work. Jan had told me that after Bronte's recovery she and Graeme sold their family home because it held too many bad memories for all of them. I loved this place, and so did Riche. I would not let that happen to us.

Riche took another few sips and again tilted the cup. More threats.

More sips. And so it went for the best part of an hour, this dark and horrible brinkmanship, until eventually Riche said he had finished and handed me the cup. This was one of those rare occasions when almost empty was enough.

'Did you bring a toothbrush for me?' He looked ready to drop.

I nodded and got the toothbrush and paste from the car. Riche scrubbed his teeth and spat into the grass, and then I held his brush for him while he rinsed his mouth with more of his Adam's Ale. When he'd finished, he gave me an enquiring look.

'You can rest on your bed. I'm going up to the cottage to make dinner for everyone else,' I said.

Riche stepped up into the caravan and stood just inside the door. He looked around, then made his way slowly down the caravan, stopping every step or two to examine the floor and check the surface of the bench. His eyes swept over the stove and then he hurried past to the rear of the caravan. He leaned forward to check the double bed mattress that took up most of the width.

'Are the sheets clean?'

'Brand new.' I mentally thanked Kevin for making sure our arrangement didn't come unstuck because of red volcanic-soil paw prints or the evidence of canine incontinence. 'And here's a fresh bottle of water for you. Make sure you drink at least half before bed.'

I removed the plastic seal from the water bottle and put it on the bench near Riche's bed, and then I went out, the door of the caravan shutting behind me with a sharp click.

I prepared a meal and carried a tray of food in to my mother, who was by now completely bedridden. She was slumped against the pillows in a faint cloud of ammonia. As I put the tray aside and began to haul her into a semi-sitting position my mother's eyes brightened and teared in a rare, heartbreaking, moment of lucidity.

'I never thought I'd end up like this,' she whispered.

The sheer random cruelty of the world left me breathless.

I knew I should sit with her and talk—surely her time on this planet was limited, and didn't I owe her at least half an hour of the comfort human presence can offer? But my reserves of kindness had been drained, and I couldn't. I just couldn't.

My father seemed hungrier for company than food, so I lingered at the table with him while Louise and Andy disappeared into their bedroom to rediscover neglected toys. When finally I looked at my watch, two hours had passed. The children and I took advantage of the running water and flushing toilet before we made our way back to the caravan, keeping watch for snakes in the drifts of leaves beneath the handkerchief tree. When we reached the caravan, I unlatched the door and walked in first to find Riche standing, tense and fidgety, by his bed. His eyes were bloodshot and his face puffy.

'You shut me in,' he sobbed. 'I wanted to go to the toilet but I couldn't touch the door handle.'

What an idiot I was. What a thoughtless, wrung-out, exhausted idiot.

'I'm sorry. So sorry.' I closed my eyes for a second. 'You can go outside now.'

'I used that.' Riche pointed to the water bottle on the bench, full, now, of golden liquid.

'Gross,' Andy said from behind me.

I took the bottle outside and emptied it onto the grass. Stress had made a moth-eaten mess of my memory and all I could do was what any mother would do when she made a mistake—resolve to do better next time. I took the bottle back in for Riche to use during the night, and then I settled the children into bed. Finally I changed into my pyjamas, snuggled up next to my daughter and fell asleep on our property for the first time in nine months, lulled by the sound of waves crashing on the shore and the wind soughing in the fig tree in front of the caravan.

Sometime after midnight, I woke with a full bladder. I let myself out of the caravan and picked my way carefully through the grass. I lowered my pyjama pants and squatted and hoped that a snake didn't bite my bare arse. Damn Kevin! While I peed by the light of the moon, he was walking out of the Palace or the Pierre and looking forward to a fashionable luncheon, maybe a Broadway show in the evening…

But was it possible that he might have preferred, as I did, to be here looking after our son rather than entrusting him to the care of strangers in rotating shifts?

Yes, I realised. It was possible.

I pulled my pants up and studied for a moment the weird beauty of the trees in the moonlight before I returned to my banquette bed.

We woke to birdcalls and sunshine. I gave Riche his protein shake and Andy and Louise their toast and Promite, then settled all three children into the car. Before I joined them, I knelt down and cuddled Minnie on our front lawn. The deciduous fig tree at the edge of the lawn was covered in fresh new leaves, a light green that would deepen within weeks to a mature forest green. Beyond the tree the Pacific Ocean sparkled and a hundred metres or so out, a humpback whale splashed the surface. The migration back to the cooler southern waters with the baby whales had begun.

I hoisted myself into the car and slid the second John Marsden tape into the cassette player as we set off. I dropped Louise at Shearwater, and then the boys and I headed for Brisbane.

The call came at 6 am on Wednesday, December 17. I was lying in bed, half-dozing in my darkened room after giving Riche his first shake for the day. I was still tired from the trip to Mullumbimby the day before, where I had spent two hours catch-up mothering Louise, and two minutes talking to my mother.

I picked up the receiver, and my father cleared his throat. I knew what he was about to tell me.

'Mum died during the night,' he said. 'The nurse found her when she came to give her her shower.' His voice cracked. 'She'd been dead a while.'

I asked, of course, if he was okay, but my words sounded dissociated to my ears. As if my feelings were in a different room. I sat up and looked at Andy, making sleepy snuffling noises on his mattress on the floor.

'I'm a bit upset,' my father conceded. 'It was…She was alone, and she vomited. I don't know if she was in pain.'

'Maybe she had a stroke and died in her sleep,' I said. Then I wondered if she'd been awake when she vomited. My poor mother.

'I'll come home,' I said, unsure what my father expected.

'Yes, good,' he said. 'It's going to be a hot day. Try not to take too long, the body might…'

'No, no, of course,' I blurted; I couldn't bear for my father to finish that sentence. 'I'll get there as soon as I can.' I paused. What else should I say? 'Want me to organise a funeral director?'

'If you don't mind.' The relief in his voice was palpable.

When I rang our Mullumbimby neighbour, Linda, with the news, she offered to check on my father and I gladly accepted.

I told Riche after his next protein shake. 'We have to go back down to Mullumbimby,' I said.

'Do we have to stay overnight?'

'No.' He was worrying about missing his appointments with Sonia. Every hour of contact with another human was precious. 'Just for the day.'

○

My mother's bedroom looked much the same as it had the day before. Her pink and grey paisley dressing gown hung over a half-open cupboard door and her bags of incontinence pads stood alongside the wheeled shower chair. Birthday cards, handkerchiefs and bottles of pills cluttered the top of the china cabinet just inside the door. When I had brought my mother's cabinet over from Perth with my parents, I had hoped its familiarity would lessen my mother's confusion in her new environment. I'd washed and dried the Royal Crown Derby dinner service and arranged the pieces on the shelves, but it didn't seem to help.

My mother lay on her bed under the window, the light calico of the lowered blinds doing little to block the sun's harsh glare. Her head was tilted to the right, her final action, a decorous turning away to vomit, preserved by rigor mortis. Linda had washed her and dressed her in a fresh nightgown, a shapeless garment of blue cotton held together at the back by ties. A posy of hibiscus and lavender lay on the pillow by her head. On the desk next to her bed, the blades of a fan spun lazily, failing to stir the heavy air. Smoke spiralled up almost undisturbed from a stick of sandalwood incense that burned on a white china plate next to it. My mother would have turned her nose up at the incense, which she associated with work-shy hippies, but she would have loved the lavender, her favourite scent for the potpourri she made before her stroke.

I reached for my mother's left hand. Her skin felt cool and dry, and her wedding and engagement rings slid easily over her bony knuckle. For two and a half years I had wanted her to die, hating to see her decline and suffer. But as I stood by her bed, her hand in mine for the last time, I felt a deep ache in my stomach. I would never hear her voice again.

The parallels between my mother and Riche struck me forcefully. They had both suffered some kind of brain problem, a control-centre malfunction. My mother had lost her life; Riche's was at present a life half lived.

Outside, the dogs started barking, and I heard a car draw up—it had to be the funeral director. Riche waited, alone, in the caravan. Would the sight of the hearse upset him? Would he look at it and realise how close he'd come to travelling in one earlier in the year? Mercifully, probably, not.

I bent and gave my mother a final kiss.

Riche didn't seem unduly distressed by the thought of my mother's body lying in the house. But he was anxious to return to Brisbane and the comforting structure of his therapy appointments and Games Workshop visits. So after I had given him his protein shake from the cooler, we got in the car and left.

o

When it was all over—the trips up and down the highway, the funeral in the sweltering heat of the ugly brick church in Brunswick Heads, the tea and sandwiches and small talk with relatives—I made the decision to return to Mullumbimby for two weeks over Christmas. The clinic would be closed for the holidays, so there was no real need to remain in Brisbane. Riche looked upset when I told him, but I promised to drive him up to Brisbane every few days to visit Games Workshop.

What I didn't tell him was that I wondered if we would be returning to Brisbane to live. Footprints of Angels, recently renamed the Bronte Foundation, had been invaluable in stabilising him, providing a safe and compassionate environment, and keeping him out of hospital. Riche's sessions had allowed me sanity-saving coffee breaks. I'd met other mothers through Footprints, felt the solidarity of shared experience. And I'd bought myself time to come to grips with Riche's illness; I'd schooled myself to be resolute in the face of its tyrannical demands. I'd had some help in this—his spitting for instance—but I'd had to figure out much of it alone, so I felt confident that I could continue without five therapy sessions a week.

The main problem was that Riche's progress had been slow. His weight gain in ten months was still only five kilograms. If we continued on this trajectory, we'd be cooling our heels in Brisbane for another couple of years. I was sure I could achieve the same results, if not better, at home in Mullumbimby. He needed more calories and the best way to get them was by reintroducing food. I didn't know how I would achieve that, but thought that normalising our lives by returning home would be a good start. Dr S, the psychiatrist, agreed.

On Christmas Eve, I packed three boxes of protein powder and a supply of soymilk for our proposed two-week trip to Mullumbimby. I shut the loudly indignant cats in a cage and strapped it in on the back seat. I dusted off the game of Risk and packed it in my bag… one just never knew. Under a blanket in the back of the car, I stashed contraband in the cooler: a precooked boned turkey roll, a Christmas pudding, a small jar of cranberry jelly, a plastic tub of brandy butter, and two ice cream containers of salad. Riche wouldn't go near the cottage, so he wouldn't know we were celebrating a carnivorous Christmas.

o

It took five days to eat the turkey. During that time, Kevin and I recalibrated our idea of happiness. No boisterous celebrations with Christmas crackers and carol singing. No visits from friends. No trips to the beach. Instead we secluded ourselves in our rainforest home and eased our way through the days as we cautiously enjoyed the fragile web of our reconstructed family.

Riche existed in and around the caravan, drinking his protein shakes, talking to his brother and reading. Unable to stand the thought of his loneliness, I continued to sleep in the caravan. Andy and Louise slept with me. Each night, Louise curled her warm little body against mine, unwilling to surrender me for a moment more than necessary. Kevin remained exiled to the house and the comfort of a queen-sized bed, accompanied by an overly affectionate spaniel with partially obstructed nasal passages.

o

On New Year's Eve, Kevin and I sipped Bollinger. The stars of the Milky Way glittered over our heads.

'What are your New Year's resolutions?' I said.

'I'm not making any.' Kevin grinned. 'That way I can't break them. Let me guess yours. You're going to get Riche better, and you're going to teach me to stop being such a stupid prick.'

'I want to move home,' I said. 'And I want to see you and Riche reconciled. It's for his sake as well as yours. A boy needs his dad. And for my sake too.'

At ten o'clock, I tucked Andy and Louise into bed in the caravan with Riche and sat with them while they dozed off. Then I rejoined

Kevin on the veranda, and we chatted until rockets and fire showers exploded to the north, trailing incandescent tails into a New Year that Kevin and I dared to hope would be better than the last. We drained our glasses, went to bed, and made love for the first time in eleven months. No great fireworks there. Just a tender salve to our relationship. Then I said goodnight to Kevin and Minnie and the other dogs and returned to the caravan.

Over the next few days, Riche lurked on the fringe of the family. He watched from beneath his veil of hair while Kevin horsed around in the swimming pool with Andy and Louise. He talked to Andy when he was playing in his sandpit. And he hovered, little more than an apparition, on the lawn in front of the cottage. But at meal times he vanished to the safety of the caravan. And it was there, after a protein shake, that I broached the subject of Kevin.

'Why don't you play a game of Risk with your father?'

Riche looked down and scuffed the carpet with his sandal.

I plunged on through his silence. 'You and Dad don't have to talk about anything except the game,' I said. 'And Dad will move your pieces where you tell him. You won't have to touch them.'

A pause.

'Okay.'

'Well, good. I'll go and find Dad.' I wanted to throw my arms around Riche and run screaming to Kevin, but I managed to keep it down to a casual stroll, my excitement compressed into a happy whistle.

Kevin gaped when I told him. 'Are you serious?' His son hadn't spoken a word to him in eleven months. 'What should I do? What should I say?'

'Don't talk about anorexia and don't, whatever you do, mention your mother,' I said. 'Wash your hands thoroughly so you don't look uncomfortable when Riche asks, and trust me, he will. And change your shirt.'

Kevin's messy eating habits were a standing joke in the family.

He didn't have an anorexic bone in his body; he ate indiscriminately and with relish. That morning, opening the mail while he ate, he'd spilled egg yolk down the front of his shirt.

'And don't forget that the object of the game is to *lose*.'

'I'm going to thrash him,' he said with a mischievous glint in his eyes.

I knew he didn't mean it. I also knew it would take him quite an effort not to win. The killer instinct was deeply ingrained in Kevin—he was, after all, an investment banker. He had occasionally reduced Louise to tears after crushing her in Monopoly.

Two hours later, Kevin walked in with a poker face. My expression must have betrayed my misgivings because he burst into delighted laughter.

'He whipped me,' he said. An indelible smile split his face and lit up his eyes. 'And he wants to play again tomorrow.'

Kevin and Riche played several games of Risk a day during the next few days. As Riche's army advanced across borders in Europe, America, Africa and Asia, other barriers fell and Kevin marched his way back into Riche's heart.

And then, one by one, barriers elsewhere in Riche's life began to fall.

On a scorching hot early January day, I noticed Riche eyeing Andy and Louise in the pool. They kicked and laughed and squirted each other in the crystal clear water. I left my chair on the veranda and went to stand next to Riche.

'Dip your foot in the water,' I said. 'It's clean.' Riche looked at me. 'And it's not making Andy and Louise fat. See for yourself.'

He swallowed.

'Go on,' I said. 'Give it a go. I'll open the gate.' I held the gate, and my breath, and waited.

Riche hung back, and I cursed my over-eagerness. But then he kicked off his sandals and walked in. He stood by the step at the shallow end of the pool. Andy and Louise looked at their brother with swimming-pool-sized eyes but said nothing, schooled in the art of restraint.

'I'll race you,' Andy said to his sister. They tore off down the pool. Riche watched. He took a step back. I stayed by the gate.

Riche looked at me, and his look eclipsed the world. When he took a step towards the pool my heart stood still. He dipped his right foot into the water. My heart juddered back into action. He held his foot in the water a moment and then lifted it out and shook it. He turned to me and smiled, a look of simple joy that chased the shadows away and let the world exist again in its kaleidoscopic glory.

I stayed silent, not daring to speak, and waited for his next move. He took a step closer to me. 'Do you think I could go for a swim?'

I spread my arms, palms up. 'Don't see why not. It's hot enough.'

'What shall I wear?'

'Your undies,' I said. 'There's no one else around.'

To my surprise, Riche pulled off his shirt and grey cotton trousers, leaving them in a heap on the ground. Dressed only in his black underpants, he climbed down onto the top step of the pool. Then he took another step down, his hands held high out of the waist-deep water. He brought his arms to his sides, plunging his hands into the water, and gently lowered his body until he was submerged to his neck. A look of delighted discovery crossed his face. He took a deep breath, closed his eyes, and went under.

I slowly exhaled. Eleven months previously, I had struggled to get Riche to drink water. Now he was swimming in it—with known meat-eaters. And it wasn't even The Original Adam's Ale Pure Australian Water.

o

Over the following days, Riche's obsessions unravelled with a speed that left me breathless. New skin grew on less-washed hands; roses bloomed in previously pale cheeks; an unfamiliar brightness lit sky-blue eyes; a firmer step tethered him to the earth. It was as if his brain had reached a critical point in recovery, a watershed beyond which obsessions could no longer thrive. The process reminded me of our handkerchief tree. It lost all its leaves and stood bare for several months and then—almost overnight, it seemed—buds appeared, the sketch of an evolving canopy. Then one day we would wake to a wash of green, as if a garden fairy had waved her wand overnight. Over the next couple of weeks, the leaves would continue to appear and deepen in colour, but it was that first rapid flush that seemed like a miracle. So it was with Riche.

He started to move his own pieces in the ongoing games of Risk he played with Kevin. He swam almost daily with his brother and sister, yelling and hooting as they competed to create the biggest splash when they dived in. His skin turned a warm golden brown. His waist-length hair was bleached light-blonde. He spent hours at a time in the sandpit with Andy discussing who knows what. One day, Trisska wandered past him. I watched unseen from the veranda as Riche followed her for a few steps. She stopped and looked back at him, wagged her tail. Riche took a step closer, bent down and patted her briefly. He stood up and stared intently at his hand, then with a shrug let it fall to his side and went back to Andy to resume his conversation. I sat down in a wicker chair—the one my mother used to sit in—and gazed at the ocean for a long time.

By now it was mid-January, a little over three weeks since we'd arrived in Mullumbimby for Christmas. The weather had been consistently hot and Riche was doing so well, Kevin and I decided to push him a little further. We invited an administrator from Louise's school and his family to join us for lunch and a swim. Riche stayed away from the table but played ball games in the pool with his siblings and the twin daughters from the other family, who happened to be the same age as Riche—twelve years old. Riche came to me later that day while I was hanging out the washing.

'Those girls were really nice,' he said. 'I think I want to go to Shearwater this year.'

I searched the sky for the right thing to say and clung to my composure. 'Great idea,' I said. *And shall we book in a spacewalk while we're at it?* 'But you'll need to eat if you want to go to school.'

'I will.' No hesitation. I realised he had already given this some thought.

'School starts in two weeks. You'll have to eat before then.'

'I will. I'll eat a sandwich for lunch next week.'

'Fine,' I said. So my boy wanted to eat after almost a year. No drama; no need to turn into a sweating, heart-thumping mess. I groped for my next move. Riche's psychiatrist had mentioned once that when Riche started eating again, I should let him choose his food as long as it made up a balanced diet that included all food groups and contained enough energy. I had no better ideas. 'What sort of sandwich?'

'White bread with Vegemite and cheese. But only thin slices. And no butter.'

'Not enough energy.' The word calorie was like nitroglycerine: it might explode in my face if handled incorrectly. Energy conveyed, or so I thought, an image of Riche running through a school playground. Or balancing on monkey bars. Was this the image it conjured for Riche, or did he see it for the euphemism it was?

'I'll have butter on one slice of bread but not the other. And not too much.'

It wasn't perfect. At the time I didn't realise just how imperfect it was. Regardless, it was a quantum leap in the right direction.

I arranged a meeting with the woman who would teach Riche at Shearwater. She said Riche could sit near the door so that he could leave the room at any time if he felt uncomfortable. His waist-length hair? Not a problem. Cooking lessons (I nearly fainted at the idea)? He could skip those and take art instead. Most importantly, someone would 'keep an eye' on Riche while he ate his lunch, although I wondered if the 'eye' would be open and focused.

With the school organised, I got underway with sandwich prep-arations. Riche stayed at home while I went to the supermarket. The smell of rotisserie chicken wafted through the aisles. Would it still

have sent Riche running, or would he have sniffed the air with interest? I wondered this as I filled my basket with a white sandwich loaf
(added omega-3 acids for Riche's brain), cheddar cheese, a tub of
canola spread and a jar of Vegemite.

At home, I busied myself with sorting the refrigerator. I used a
simple system: anything with a fungal growth I tossed. Everything
else I shunted to the top or bottom shelves, taking care to bury the
kangaroo meat under my father's Sara Lee apricot crumble, leaving
the middle shelf—scrubbed clean with warm, lemon-fresh water—
empty, an uncontaminated safe-haven for Riche's food.

Next I cleared and scrubbed the kitchen bench and set out the
breadboard. I felt like a priest preparing for a celebratory sacrament.
Before I could get started with making the sandwich, Riche appeared
on the kitchen veranda, the closest he'd come to entering our cottage
since our move to Brisbane.

'You can't watch me,' I said.

'Make sure you only put butter on one slice,' he said.

'Yes, yes—of course.' I shooed him away, fixed the sandwich, put
it on a plate and carried it out to Riche.

'Eat it or else,' I said in a business-like tone.

Riche picked up the sandwich, inspected it, and took a bite. My
heart seemed to be ricocheting wildly behind my ribs. Riche chewed
two or three times and then swallowed. His face bore a look of intense
concentration. I watched closely as his Adam's apple slid up and
down. Waited to see if his cheeks bulged. They didn't. Another bite
followed, and another, until Riche had eaten every last crumb. His
first solid lunch in over a year. I took the plate from him and rinsed it,
warm water flowing over my hands, warm blood gradually slowing
in my veins.

The following week, Riche started school. Each day he took a
cheese and Vegemite sandwich for lunch and roasted chickpeas for
morning tea. At the beginning of the second week, he ate a bowl of
Ginger Zing cereal with Sanitarium no-fat soymilk—red carton, of

course—instead of his breakfast protein shake. Towards the end of the second week, he added dinner to his routine—stir-fried teriyaki tofu and vegetables with rice. He had some fruit for afternoon tea and ditched the last of the protein shakes. Somewhere along the way, almost unnoticed among these seismic shifts, he started drinking tap water.

In week three, Riche volunteered for the unthinkable adventure of a five-day white-water rafting camp with his school class. He returned with a glowing face and photographs of him rushing down some foaming torrent on a rubber tyre-tube. I asked about his meals. He said he had watched the amount of food other boys put on their plates and had followed suit. I decided against weighing him, not wanting to re-ignite that particular obsession—but I could see from the look of him that he hadn't lost weight. In fact, didn't he look just the tiniest bit heavier?

○

Each day of Riche's illness felt like a year and a long year at that. After that mid-January decision to go to Shearwater, time collapsed.

Eleven weeks, three hair-trimming sessions (by me), countless boxes of Ginger Zing, kilograms of tofu; loaves of Vegemite and cheese sandwiches flashed by. In April, Kevin and I found ourselves in hard plastic chairs before an outdoor stage at Shearwater Steiner School, the stars above pressed like jewels into the velvety sky. Louise, now seven, roamed with packs of children dressed in rainbow-coloured clothing on the grassy slope behind the seating. Andy stood ten metres from us, still silent and watchful, not yet ready to trust this new reign of calm.

Riche had announced several weeks previously that he was performing in the choir during the school cabaret. That was nice. The real bombshell had come just that morning, on the day of the performance, over his bowl of Ginger Zing.

'I have a solo,' he said.

'Great.' My standard, scrupulously unsurprised answer. 'What is it?'

'Just a solo.' Just another heart-stopping everyday miracle.

I shivered in the cool evening air and waited for Riche's first public performance since his illness. I wondered if he was pushing himself too hard. He had missed an entire year of schooling and had been at Shearwater for just nine weeks. And there'd been hitches. Like the day Louise said a girl asked why Riche stepped back whenever anyone tried to get close enough to talk. I had talked to Riche, explained that this was an unusual way to behave, that he should hold his ground when people spoke to him because they wouldn't hurt him. The next day Riche reported back that he had tried it and it had worked. He had similarly reprogrammed other facets of his behaviour, showing enormous courage. But a solo performance?

An instrumental piece finished, and the choir filed onstage. Riche stood in the front row, towards the side. In his shorts and dark grey T-shirt, he looked thin rather than emaciated. Tonight he wore his hair parted down the middle, the fringe, for the first time, tucked behind his ears, his pale face turned to the choir mistress. She lifted her baton and twenty voices sang in unison.

When the first song finished, the children drew themselves up and launched into the Black Eyed Peas song 'Where is the Love'. All except Riche held a printout of the lyrics. His dog-eared copy stuck out of his pocket. The choir reached the second verse, and Riche stepped forward. His intense blue eyes stared straight out at the crowd. The murmuring in the audience subsided, and everyone turned to watch this fragile little white boy rap his heart out about war and suffering and youth dying young. And there was no doubt in my mind that on that night, the love was with my son. People around me smiled, eyes glistened with tears, and Kevin and I wept. Riche faltered over a word and frowned. I held my breath, but his face relaxed and he sang on.

Afterwards, we met the choir mistress.

'Riche's my golden-haired boy,' she said.

If only the paediatrician in Brisbane could hear those words. I could imagine her mouth opening in surprise, and her lips turning up in a smile as she saw the transformation in the boy who had screamed at his mother that she was a fucking idiot.

The smell of hot soup and coffee lured me to several trestle tables near the Year 4 classroom veranda. As I neared the tables, I saw Riche waiting to be served—the first food or drink purchase I had seen him make since before his illness. I stepped back, afraid that if he saw me, the spell would be broken. He spoke to a woman who, from her easy manner, was obviously unaware of the importance of the sale she was about to make. Riche counted out some coins and handed them to her. She passed him a paper cup of apple juice.

Riche held the cup as if it contained the most expensive French champagne money could buy. He moved away from the crowd and looked at the drink for a second or two. I waited for him to change his mind. Instead he brought the cup to his lips and drained it in a few swift gulps. I slumped on a nearby plastic chair and succumbed once more to tears.

Later that night I stood in the garden and watched a trail of moonlight as soft and luminous as a swathe of satin stretch itself across the ocean towards the horizon. A steady cycle of waves washed onto the shore. Riche got out of the car and yawned. He peered towards the caravan, cloaked in darkness.

'I'm tired,' he said. 'Can I sleep in Grandma's bed tonight?'

The car keys slipped from my fingers and clattered to the ground. I stooped and searched for them, glad of the excuse to hide my face. 'I'll just find some sheets.'

Riche disappeared to the bathroom. Kevin held out a hand to help me up.

'Did that really just happen? He wants to sleep in the bed your mother died in?'

I took some sheets to my mother's room. It had changed a little in the last four months; no more incontinence pads or shower chair. And I could see the china cabinet moving to the loungeroom soon, too, to make way for a boy's desk.

For me, days, weeks, months of tears followed the night of Riche's performance. I cried at sad movies, road-kill, grey skies, my reflection in the mirror and most things Kevin said. I cried for no reason at all, and everything was a reason to cry. Obituaries in the *Sydney Morning Herald* became my daily pleasure. I refused to dye my greying hair, never wore makeup, and dressed in navy-blue, black, brown and grey. It took me a while to realise I had developed post-traumatic stress disorder and longer to realise Kevin had too.

Riche, meanwhile, continued to improve. He surprised me with a question over breakfast, a month or so after the school cabaret.

'Do you think I could get dreadlocks?' His voice was shy, hesitant. 'The salon in town does them.'

I made an appointment. After eighteen months of refusing to visit a hairdressing salon, Riche sat for three hours in a cloud of hairspray while a hairdresser twisted and twirled his hair into dreadlocks: the ultimate recovery hairstyle.

Kevin by now was seeing a therapist; I turned to writing. Riche had told me months before that he didn't want me to write about his illness—but I needed to understand better for myself the events of the last two and a half years, and I thought writing would help me do this.

Eventually I asked Riche if he knew the subject of my writing.

'Of course,' he said. 'You're writing about us.'

'Do you mind?'

'I've got two conditions.' He gave me a stern look. 'No pornography. And I get ten percent of your earnings.'

I laughed. Did Riche not realise that his illness was the most effective anti-aphrodisiac I'd encountered in twenty years of marriage?

The following year I discovered a book called *Eating with Your Anorexic* by Laura Collins, an American woman whose daughter had suffered from anorexia. After a few brushes with the 'dysfunctional family' model Laura came across the Family Based Therapy approach, which I'd read about briefly many months earlier.

This approach, I learned, was not lightweight quackery. Two of the major researchers in the field, Daniel Le Grange and James Lock, came from the University of Chicago and Stanford University respectively. When I first started reading about it, it was the only treatment for anorexia that had been shown to be effective through properly conducted scientific studies. As far as I know, in 2012 it still is.

In addition to writing the book, Laura had started an online parent forum: Families Empowered and Supporting Treatment of Eating Disorders—F.E.A.S.T. By now I had internet access, so each day before the rest of the family woke up I logged onto the forum. It was as if I had found my tribe. I sipped peppermint tea and rubbed my toes against Minnie's warm coat as she lay at my feet while I read other people's stories.

At the time of my first brief encounter with the FBT approach, harried, exhausted and discouraged, I'd wondered how anyone could possibly subject herself, their family, to its demands. Now, at the other end of a process I could see had been at least as disruptive for my family, it made sense to me. Working with the FBT method, a child with anorexia ate his or her meals with the family, and life basically stopped until the child finished the meal. The FBT mantra is: 'The food needs to be eaten before you leave the table.' The child didn't go to school until breakfast was eaten. If breakfast landed on the floor, another plate of food appeared in front of the child. If the child tried to leave the room, a parent blocked his or her exit. If breakfast took four hours to eat, morning tea followed immediately. If that took two hours, it ran into lunch. Instead of banishing parents, the FBT approach put them in the kitchen, and with their child at the diningroom table, whether or not the child accepted his or her illness. The mystery of how to treat a sufferer in denial was solved.

Parents gave up jobs where necessary, they called on family and friends to provide constructive help—an outing for a neglected sibling, high-energy food baked with love—they cancelled social engagements and holiday trips. They did all these things with medical monitoring and the support of FBT-trained family therapists who met with the parents, and sometimes the siblings, as well as the sick child.

It took me a while to understand the differences between this form of treatment and the punitive measures still used by many hospitals. The key difference, I decided, is achievable goals. The traditional approach asks an anorexic child to do all the things it takes over the course of, say, a week to gain a certain amount of weight in order to earn a telephone call from a friend. It's like asking them to hurdle an impossible height, knowing it will require an interminable run-up—and on the other side of the hurdle they will land in a bed of nails.

Asking that same child to eat one meal at a time is a concrete, achievable goal, particularly in the home environment with people they trust—their parents—to supervise the meal with steadfast love and, crucially, to keep at it for as long as it takes. In those circumstances, parents can overcome a child's initial resistance in a surprisingly short time, sometimes even days.

Now, at last, I saw that the parents on the forum were doing much the same thing with their children that I had done with Riche. The critical difference was that they used real food where I had used protein shakes. With no sense of self-blame—how could I have known?—I saw other differences, such as the faster rate of weight gain expected. To achieve this, most parents allowed the children no choice at all, at least in the early stages of weight restoration. Many advised banning the child from the kitchen. This relieved sick children of the responsibility for making decisions. Parents never 'needed' to lie. They all knew exactly how many calories their child was consuming. Another difference I saw was in the understanding of how the illness worked. The 'negative mind' of Footprints was in actual fact a mind trapped in obsessive thoughts because of starvation.

I was confused by the fact that Riche's mental state had improved so dramatically so quickly after a year of being unwell, even though he was still very underweight—most forum parents reported that the mental state improvement lagged behind the weight gain. Then I came across an explanation from Daniel Le Grange, who said that just as each time a child restricted his food intake, he or she helped to solidify new neurological patterns—restricting patterns—so too each bite, or in Riche's case each mouthful of protein shake, helped reverse these changes. As I had suspected, the protein shakes were a better alternative to passive nasogastric feeds.

The parent forum became an obsession for me. As the months became years, I sat at my desk in the corner of my bedroom every single day and logged on. I felt less alone and I continued to learn. An article on WebMD in 2005, *Anorexia and Bulimia: Cracking the Genetic Code*, discussed the likelihood of a genetic vulnerability to anorexia. That news began a process of healing in me, and in my marriage. Both Kevin and I had made mistakes, that much had never been in doubt. But now I knew that these mistakes would not have led to anorexia in a child with different genes.

I learned, too, that obsessive-compulsive tendencies were a fairly common precursor to anorexia, and I remembered the long trail of Riche's obsessive habits that seemed to intensify in the months prior to the onset of anorexia—his tennis-ball bouncing and cheek popping.

Years later, I would rediscover a newspaper article from around that time that I had clipped out and pasted, in a gesture of defiance, on the inside cover of Kathryn Zerbe's parent-blaming text *The Body Betrayed*. The unidentified article (it most likely came from the *Sydney Morning Herald*) read: 'A "significant association" between anorexia and the genes HTR1D and OPRD1 was found by researchers at 10 universities in Britain and the US.' And I would feel the familiar sense of relief that attended any evidence for the proposition that I had not single-handedly brought my son to the brink of death.

Through the forum I understood, finally, that my habit of blaming Kevin and his mother mirrored the traditional approach that blamed parents. It didn't lead to a single gram of weight gain in my son; instead, it nearly destroyed my marriage and it led to a rift with Kevin's family that is unresolved even now. I accept that I will probably never know exactly what acted as an environmental trigger for Riche. At the same time, I know that any talk of restrictive eating is unwise in our household.

Most of all, the F.E.A.S.T. forum shone a light for me on the future of anorexia treatment. How much better Riche's outcome might have been if I had known of the FBT approach. If I had known that a doctor would refer me to a family therapist rather than admit my son to hospital, I would not have wasted so much time looking for compassionate help. Riche's physical health would not have deteriorated so dramatically and his psychological symptoms might not have become so severe. If I had known that short-term hospitalisation to stabilise him was an option, I would have taken it. And then taken my son home to continue his weight restoration.

How much better it would have been for our family if a wise family therapist had helped me to put blame aside, and helped Kevin to reach out to Riche very early on in his illness. On a larger scale, think of the dollars to be saved in the health-care system if weight restoration at home was supported, rather than months of costly in-patient care.

There will always be a place for in-patient care. Some families, for financial or other reasons, are not in a position to care for seriously ill children at home. But it would be so much better to have the choice.

A statement made by Thomas R. Insel MD, Director of the (US) National Institute of Mental Health, appeared on the forum in 2006. In it, he said that eating disorders had 'a biological core, with genetic components, changes in brain activity, and neural pathways currently under study'.

In 2007, he wrote of the past (and in many cases, current) practice of excluding and blaming parents: 'We need to ask for a day of atonement for past care, and we need to bring families into the picture and to make patient care much more individualised.'

Finally, the tears I wept were of happiness.

Riche's baby book contains, along with the list of favourite animals that included single-celled organisms, all the usual milestones: he smiled on Monday, May 6, he waved a yellow telephone-shaped rattle in the air at six weeks, he went on his first holiday (to Montauk, Long Island) on the Labor Day weekend in May 1991.

Fourteen years later, milestones of a different sort continued to accumulate during Riche's ongoing recovery: a post-anorexia trek on Hinchinbrook Island, the first fish meal, the first lollies, and his first appearance as a rock-n-roll dancer in the school's annual wearable arts performance.

○

In December 2007 Riche is accepted into boarding school on the east coast of the US. He has decided that he wants to take full advantage of his US citizenship and see the world. On the weekend before Christmas, he announces his intention to start eating meat. Kevin and I exchange looks. We have no philosophical objection to vegetarianism, but in Riche's case, it is so entwined with his anorexia. Besides, boarding school will be easier on a less restrictive diet.

For the momentous first taste of flesh, Louise suggests chicken: she's a white meat girl. Kevin, Andy and I advise lamb chops. They taste delicious, we tell Riche. They melt in your mouth. Nothing beats a barbecued lamb chop. Riche agrees to barbecued lamb chops for his first meat meal in five and a half years.

'Let's do it tonight,' Kevin says to me. 'We don't want to risk him changing his mind.'

He wraps his arms around me and pulls me in. My cheek rubs against the worn fabric of his T-shirt—a souvenir from a surfing trip last year to the Malawi islands in Indonesia. He's no longer aggressively lean: he gave up the Atkins diet around the time Atkins died. Kevin kisses the top of my head, and I breathe in his familiar scent. Perhaps tonight…*ten percent, and no pornography.*

Two hours later, the smell of barbecuing meat mingles with the smell of roasting potatoes. I go to the refrigerator to find the broccoli and note that the door needs cleaning. A grubby six-year-old photo of relatives, a poster of dangerous spiders and a magnetic NASA space-man with a selection of magnetic outfits cover the surface. Mould and the odd dried dribble of food complete a picture of benign neglect. I hum a tune from Mattafix, the latest favourite at my local cafe, and open the door, an action that no longer makes me break into a sweat. Riche walks into the kitchen and stands beside me.

'You should never sing, Mum,' he says. The dreadlocks are long gone. These days, he sports a buzz-cut and he towers over me. 'You're tone deaf, and a forty-seven-year-old singing Mattafix reeks of midlife crisis.'

But his words carry no sting. Last night, Riche listened while Andy and I discussed the merits of a Shearwater teacher. Riche piped up.

'She's not as good as Mum,' he said. 'Mum's the best.'

I know he doesn't always think that, but sometimes is enough. I idly swing the door in and out. The inside of the refrigerator is not much better than the door. The garbage collector comes tomorrow, so I guess tonight I'll clean out the takeaway containers of leftover

Mongolian lamb and the week-old sausages. I notice an opened packet of ham next to the spinach and ricotta agnolotti. I move the ham to the shelf above, but it's nothing more than an old habit, and I don't bother to look over my shoulder to see if Riche is watching. I take the broccoli out of the vegetable keeper. In a few minutes, it's washed and chopped and in the microwave. The potatoes look ready—crisp and brown and shiny with oil. I take them out of the oven and put them in a celadon bowl. I set the table and put a bottle of tomato sauce and a crystal dish of sticky mint jelly, a bright green that screams 'chemical additives', in the middle alongside the potatoes. The broccoli steams in its glass bowl. As an afterthought, I put a bottle of sweet chili sauce in front of my father's place.

Riche sits at the table, a comic in his hand. He needs a rest from his latest obsession—physics. Andy comes up from his room where he has been playing on his computer. He sits next to Riche and within seconds they're laughing over a page in the comic. Louise runs in from the garden, grass in her hair. She hugs me on her way to the table: so far the psychiatrist's prediction that her youth is on my side have proven to be true. My father, sporting a few extra kilograms since ditching my diet, comes in from the veranda, followed by a canine entourage.

Kevin brings in a tray of mouthwatering sausages and lamb chops. He sets the tray down in front of Riche and hands Riche a pair of tongs.

Five people suddenly busy themselves with the task of heaping potatoes and broccoli onto their plates and deliberately don't notice as Riche chooses three chops and a couple of sausages. He helps himself to roast potatoes and broccoli and squirts tomato sauce over the sausages. Minnie whines at my father's side; she knows her impatience will be rewarded.

Riche cuts a large chunk of lamb chop and spears it with his fork. He lifts the fork and, holding it midway between the plate and his mouth, examines the meat. I swear I hear a collective inhale as he takes a bite.

He chews. He swallows.

I can't help myself. 'Do you like it?'

Riche shrugs and takes another bite. 'I can't see what all the fuss is about.'

Acknowledgments

I give my heartfelt thanks to the following people.

For inspirational teaching: my dear friend Sarah Armstrong from my Mullumbimby writers' group, who taught me how to write a scene and saw me through the first draft; Kyle Minor, who saw the gaps and opened my eyes to a wealth of literature; and Ana Maria Spagna, beloved mountain woman, who helped me find my voice and planted the question, 'What does this mean?' For giving me two of these great teachers: Gotham Writers' Workshop. Thanks also to Xu Xi, Robin Hemley, Luis Francia, Ravi Shankar and Justin Hill from the City University of Hong Kong MFA program.

For feedback, cheerleading and a ready supply of tissues, various incarnations of writing groups: the infamous Level 56, Flick Creekers, fellow Gothamites especially Alex Morgan and Charlotte de Kanter Chung who have been there from the beginning. More recently, the other members of my Mullumbimby group: Jesse Blackadder, Hayley Katzen and Emma Ashmere.

For support and time with other writers: Bread Loaf Writers' Conference (Michael Collier) and Varuna (Peter Bishop and Helen Barnes-Bulley), The Healing Art of Writing workshop (David Watts) and the Northern Rivers Writers' Centre.

For practical help that gave me peace of mind: my beloved father and dogsitter extraordinaire Stan Webster and Phillip Harper and Melissa Keddie.

For publishing slightly modified extracts from this book: the editors of *Hunger Mountain*, *Alimentum* and *Bacopa Literary Review* and (forthcoming) *Black Warrior Review*, and the University of California Press in *The Healing Art of Writing*.

For keeping my head more or less screwed onto my shoulders: Amanda Ressom.

For coffee, poached eggs and good cheer to start my writing day: the staff at the Poinciana, especially Rachael Harrison, Nicole Webb and Jay Penfold. Also, Rowena, Salinya Lerdscupagorn, Anelia Mintcheva and Peter Apostolatos from Bondi Junction who took up where the Mullumbimby team left off.

For kindly agreeing to read the FBT sections, Professor Daniel Le Grange. All responsibility is mine.

In addition, I've been blessed with a fabulous agent in Lyn Tranter and an unstinting publicist in Jane Novak. I'm very grateful. Mandy Brett has been a wise and wonderful editor and a great teacher. I'm indebted to her for plucking me from the slush pile and for making the reconstructive surgery relatively painless with her compassion, wisdom and unflagging sense of humour.

For loyal and loving friendship and a ready lick: Minnie.

And, most of all, for their endless patience and general awesomeness and for allowing me to tell the story of what we as a family refer to as the attack of the killer calories: Kevin, Riche, Andy and Louise.